Your
AGELESS MIND

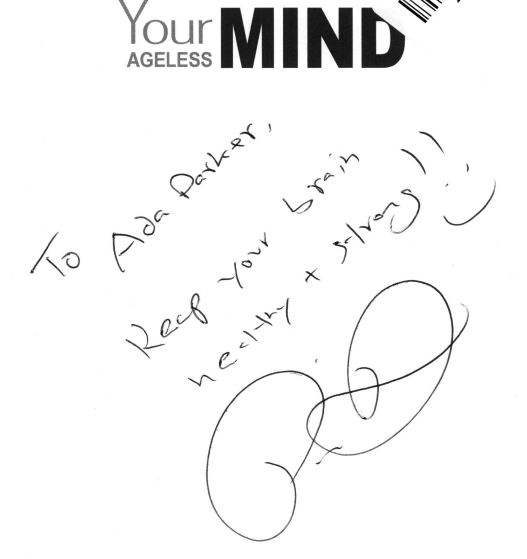

To Ada Parker,

Keep your brain
healthy + strong!!

Your AGELESS MIND

The **Complete Guide** to a **Strong, Young, Healthy Mind**

Patrick Hartory

Ireland Press
Cleveland, Ohio

This book presents nutrition and exercise information that may or may not be right for you. In view of the complex, individual, and specific nature of health and fitness problems, this book is not intended to replace professional medical advice, nor does it constitute a doctor-patient relationship. Every individual is different. Before starting any diet, meditation, or exercise program, get your doctor's approval. The information in this book is current as of 2012 and is provided for informational purposes only. The publisher and author expressly disclaim any responsibility for loss or risk incurred as a consequence of the application of the contents of this book.

Library of Congress Cataloging-in-Publication Data
Hartory, Patrick
Your ageless mind: the complete guide to a strong, young, healthy mind / Patrick Hartory
    p.   cm.
Includes bibilographical references.
ISBN 978-0-615-70269-8
1. Cognition - Age factors. 2. Memory - Age factors. 3. Brain - Aging. I. Title.
BF724.55.H45 2012
155.67 13-dc23

First Printing, January 2013
Printed in the United States of America

10 9 8 7 6 5 4 3 2 1

For my wife, Amanda, and her loving support
and for my parents who gave me my start.

Contents

There is a fountain of youth:
it is your mind,
your talents, the creativity you bring to your life
and the lives of people you love.
When you learn to tap this source,
you will have truly defeated age.

Sophia Loren

INTRODUCTION

Standing behind the volunteer booth at the community picnic, Sally flags down bystanders as she makes her sales pitch. The sun, absent since morning, has now given over to light rain as families stick close to the covered areas. "What a glorious day!" She announces. "The only thing that could make it better is a homemade slice of pie." In that moment, the dismal afternoon seems to shine a bit more brightly.

Sally is ninety-two. And what she may lack in stature (standing all of five feet tall), she makes up in youthful charisma. According to her own personal description, she has "been there, done it, and bought the tee-shirt."

A child of the Great Depression, Sally remembers helping her mother bake and sew blankets for the less fortunate in her town. Service is one of her core principles: service to neighbors, community, and country. Whether it's saying kind words to a stranger, helping her grandchildren, or fundraising for the church, when Sally talks about giving, her eyes light up as if she'd found the greatest secret of all. "There's nothing more rewarding than giving," she enthuses. "What you get back is so much greater than what you give!"

Sally's mind is sharp. She excels in bridge and enjoys spirited debates about politics and social issues. She proudly remembers names, faces, and personal details with ease – an ability she claims to work on daily. "It helps if you like people... and I like people."

Sally starts her day with twenty minutes of stretching, sit-ups, and then a short walk with her dog, Lolly. Her mental exercise includes jotting down some of her life stories in a journal. "All of my stories are going to be in a proper book someday so that I can read them when I get old," she muses.

Although she has some physical ailments, you'd never know it. If asked, she will steer the conversation to a brighter topic. "When the conversation starts going south," she says, "I change the subject. Who has time to complain?"

I asked Sally about her secret to a healthy mind. "Never stop learning," she says. "Whatever you do, stay connected to people. Practice the Golden Rule. And, (with a mischievous twinkle in her clear blue eyes), a little flirting doesn't hurt either."

Your Ageless Mind

Sally is not alone. As more and more older adults are staying active longer, we have started to change the way we look at aging. Over the past three decades, a paradigm shift has taken place in the field of neuroscience. This shift has shattered everything we once believed to be true about the aging brain.

Most of us were raised with faulty ideas about our mental capacity – such as the notion that the brain stops producing new cells and that memory and learning ability inevitably decline with age.

These notions, based on the scientific understandings of days gone by, represent harmful myths that can stifle our ability to flourish in the second half of life. In the past thirty years, the evidence supporting the notion that your mind can improve has become overwhelming. In fact, the question is no longer *whether* your mind can improve with age, but rather, *how* you can optimize your mental powers throughout life.

This book presents current, practical, evidence-based information to help you maintain a strong, young, healthy mind throughout your life. Just as Sally has intuitively done, you will learn the strategies that help support brain function, prevent disease, and avoid cognitive decline.

Baseball legend Satchel Paige once asked, "How old would you be if you didn't know how old you are?" As we know, much of life has to do with attitude. It is my hope that upon completing this book, you will have newfound confidence and optimism as you discover how to improve your ageless mind today, tomorrow, and for many years to come.

PART ONE

Your Ageless Health

When people think about staying mentally fit, they generally think about the neck up. But maintaining your ageless mind has as much to do with proper sleep and exercise as it does with improving memory. Just as your brain controls all the parts of your body, so too does the care of your body contribute to a reduced risk of memory loss, cognitive decline, and Alzheimer's disease. In these first few chapters, we will take a closer look at Alzheimer's disease, as well as some areas vital to brain health.

CHAPTER ONE

Alzheimer's & Dementia

> " *Alzheimer's... it is a barren disease, as empty and lifeless as a desert. It is a thief of hearts and souls and memories.* "
>
> **Nicholas Sparks**

ALZHEIMER'S DISEASE

Every seven seconds, someone is diagnosed with dementia. Alzheimer's disease is the most common form of dementia in adults over the age of 65, occurring in over 35 million people worldwide. Few of us can expect to remain untouched in some way by this tragic disease. While some have already experienced its attack upon a friend or family member, many of us are concerned about our own risk.

Alzheimer's is a progressive disease that affects cognitive function in multiple areas of the brain. It begins with gradual memory loss followed by a decline in the ability to perform routine tasks, disorientation, difficulty in learning, loss of language skills, impairment of judgment, and personality changes. As the disease progresses, people with Alzheimer's become unable to care for themselves, and the continual loss of brain function leads to the failure of other systems in the body, ultimately resulting in death in three to twenty years from the onset of symptoms.

As the life span in the United States and other industrialized nations continues to increase, Alzheimer's disease has emerged as one of the most common brain disorders. For all the fear and destruction it brings, however, Alzheimer's disease is a relative newcomer among the known degenerative brain diseases.

Alzheimer's - A Brief History

In 1906, the German pathologist and neurologist Alois Alzheimer treated a fifty-one-year-old woman, "Auguste D.," who developed confusion, memory loss, and psychotic symptoms that seemed to rapidly progress. Following her death four years later, Dr. Alzheimer succeeded in taking sections of her brain and staining them so that they could be examined under a microscope. While inspecting the brain tissue, he observed abnormal waxy protein fragments that he called ***amyloid plaques*** and densely twisted bundles of fiber that he named ***neurofibrillary tangles***. These microscopic deposits were scattered throughout her brain, but were especially prominent in areas that control memory and other mental functions such as language, decision-making, and personality. Dr. Alzheimer would later label this apparent illness "The Disease of Forgetfulness."

Despite the fact that Dr. Alzheimer noted its signature signs in 1906, medical research of the disease lay dormant for decades. Physicians treating the elderly simply accepted that cognitive decline was a normal part of the aging process and diagnosed them with senility. It wouldn't be until the late 1960's that neurologists, led by Dr. Robert Katzman of Albert Einstein University, began to study these older brains. Just as Dr. Alzheimer observed years earlier, they found the same tiny waxy plaques and tangled threads of *tau* protein (a type of protein) in brains of people who had died from this same condition. In fact, the older, most senile brains were entirely filled with these plaques and tangles. As a result of these studies, this type of senility was finally termed "Alzheimer's disease."

After that, an epidemic of Alzheimer's disease was declared and the world recognized that senility was not just a regular part of aging. It was a disease attacking brain cells – and it was fatal.

Plaques and Tangles

No one knew how to stop the disease's relentless infiltration throughout the brains of these patients. They did know, however, that amyloid plaques and tau neurofibrillary tangles were a key part of the story.

When neuropathologists looked at hundreds of autopsied brains from people who died at various ages, they found only a few scattered plaques and tangles in people who died in their 20's; but in the brains of people who died a decade older, they found more, establishing a correlation between the age of a healthy brain and the number of Alzheimer's plaques and tangles it contained. The pattern of distribution was consistent with Alois Alzheimer's early findings indicating that the disease begins in specific memory centers deep within the brain, spreading to other memory and thinking regions in the brain's outer rim. As the disease progresses, many patients begin to lose short-term memory, then long-term, and then often experiencing notable changes in personality – the core of what defines them as an individual.

Nearly all of us have some plaques and tangles in our brains, but they don't begin to affect us until the accumulation reaches a critical threshold – a tipping point when our brains can no longer compensate for the misfiring neurons.

A Contributing Factor: Inflammation and Oxidation

Inflammation and oxidation contribute to the progression of Alzheimer's disease, just as they do in heart disease, cancer, and aging itself.

Inflammation is generally a good thing, signifying that the body is working to heal itself, but sometimes too much of a good thing can be harmful. At a cellular level, inflammation can mean that the body is attacking a foreign object, irritation, or infection. This leads the way toward healing a wound or killing off the offending bacteria or virus. But when scientists looked more closely at the amyloid plaques found in Alzheimer's brains, they discovered evidence of excessive inflammation, including *cytokines*, the tiny protein molecules that attack foreign material. Researchers are now finding a connection between Alzheimer's and elevated levels of these cytokine proteins.

Oxidation has also been recognized as a factor in the pathology of Alzheimer's disease. Oxidation is a process that can be observed in the browning of a sliced apple or the rusting of an old bicycle left outdoors. In our bodies, oxidation is necessary for our cells to do their work, but the process results in by-products known as oxidants or *free radicals*. Like all of the body's cells, brain cells undergo wear and tear from these free radicals, which can damage the genetic material of otherwise healthy cells. This oxidative stress accelerates nearly all age-related diseases from cancer to cataracts to Alzheimer's disease.

Later chapters will explain how food can help combat free radicals in the body. Studies have found a link between brain health and the foods, medicines, and lifestyle choices that help to reduce inflammation. Consuming antioxidant fruit and vegetables is a critical component of a diet that protects us from Alzheimer's disease. This book will show you how diet and lifestyle choices can support better brain health.

The Genetic Element

Scientists don't yet fully understand what causes Alzheimer's. The more they learn about this devastating disease, however, the more they realize that genetics play an important role in its development.

With Alzheimer's disease, no one really knows precisely if or when symptoms will strike during his or her lifetime. In rare situations, a genetic mutation found in less than 1% of the population can result in *early-onset* Alzheimer's disease, occurring before age 60. This rare occurrence can a cause a cluster of cases among middle-aged relatives.

> **AGELESS MIND FACT**
>
> Gene mutations can trigger toxic levels of *beta* amyloid in the brain - a precursor to Alzheimer's plaques.

The rest of us don't have to worry about this "Alzheimer's gene." The most common occurrence is *late-onset* Alzheimer's disease, occurring after age 60. Since it is not caused by a genetic mutation, it is difficult to accurately calculate someone's risk. Scientists can, however, apply the knowledge gained from population studies to derive some rough estimates. These studies have identified two factors that contribute to an increased risk of developing Alzheimer's: whether an individual has an affected first-degree relative, such as a parent or sibling, and the age at which that relative developed Alzheimer's. For example, if a parent develops Alzheimer's in his sixties, the child has a higher risk than if the onset were in the parent's eighties. Studies also suggest that having more than one first-degree relative with Alzheimer's disease increases the risk. If no family history of Alzheimer's is present, there is approximately a 10% lifetime risk of developing the disease, while a family history among close relatives can elevate one's lifetime risk to 20%.

The bottom line is that our DNA does not tell the whole story. "It's highly unlikely that genes alone influence whether you get the disease," says Dr. Gerard Schellenberg from the University of Pennsylvania. "There is almost certainly a combination of genes and something in the environment – such as diet, lifestyle, or head trauma – that we don't yet understand." For now, the non-genetic lifestyle choices that we make every day may be the biggest factor in avoiding Alzheimer's disease.

Alzheimer's Disease Prevention

We can estimate the potential impact of a healthy lifestyle on our risk for Alzheimer's disease by looking at previous studies that have demonstrated a connection between these habits and future risk for the disease. From these results, we can estimate that spending time engaged in such habits may delay the onset of symptoms, perhaps by years. For example, a recent study indicated that physical exercise several times a week over a two-year period lowered a person's future risk for memory decline by 46%. Eating antioxidant fruits and vegetables such as blueberries and broccoli for a four-year period reduced dementia risk by 44%. People who spent time doing complex mental tasks during mid-life decreased dementia risk by as much as 48%.

Throughout this book you will hear about these and similar studies and learn how lifestyle strategies can forestall the effects of Alzheimer's disease. The sooner you start to protect your brain against Alzheimer's, the sooner you will notice improvement – not only in recall and mental focus, but also in energy level, mood, and general health and well-being.

ALZHEIMER'S AND DEMENTIA

People often use "dementia" and "Alzheimer's disease" interchangeably, but the two words do not mean the same thing. Dementia describes a cluster of symptoms from a loss of cognitive skills – thinking, remembering, and reasoning – that is so severe the person has trouble carrying out daily activities.

Dementia is a category of disease. Saying a person has dementia is like saying a person has cancer. Well, what kind of cancer? One could have leukemia, lymphoma, sarcoma, carcinoma, or melanoma, for example. Likewise, there are many types of dementia.

While Alzheimer's disease is the most common form of dementia, it only accounts for between 50 and 70% of all cases.

When is it Not Alzheimer's?

Dementia usually is caused by a disease or underlying medical condition. Sometimes it results from neurodegenerative diseases like Alzheimer's disease or Parkinson's disease. While Alzheimer's disease may be the most common cause of dementia, it is far from the only cause. A stroke in the memory or language part of the brain also can create cognitive impairments that constitute dementia, but this dementia, a result of vascular disease, is referred to as ***vascular dementia***. In some cases, dementia has a treatable cause. For example, the cumulative side effects of medications taken for other medical conditions can diminish the ability to remember and think. Depression, blood clots pressing on the brain, and metabolic imbalances also can lead to a dementia-like condition.

All types of dementia are characterized by cognitive decline (such as memory, orientation, and executing tasks) that affect daily life, but each type of dementia has different features that distinguish one kind from another. These differences are important, since they each require different diagnoses and treatment plans.

Vascular Dementia

The second most common type of dementia (after Alzheimer's) is vascular dementia. Vascular dementia is caused by poor blood circulation to the brain, depriving brain cells of the nutrients and oxygen they need to function normally. Common symptoms of memory loss and cognitive decline can occur either suddenly, following a stroke, or over time, through a series of small strokes. It is often associated with focal weakness, loss of coordination, and trouble with balance. This type of dementia may not progress and can even improve with the right type of treatment.

Dementia with Lewy bodies (DLB)

Sometimes referred to as Lewy body disease, this type of dementia is characterized by the production of abnormal protein deposits called ***Lewy bodies***. First identified by neurologist Frederic Lewy, these spherical structures develop inside nerve cells and lead to the degeneration of brain tissue. This degeneration disrupts the brain's normal functioning, impairing cognition, behavior, and sometimes causing tremors. Symptoms include slow movement and Parkinson's-like features (stiffness and shakiness), as well as experiencing visual hallucinations. DLB is not reversible and has no known cure.

Fronto-Temporal Dementia (FTD)

Fronto-temporal dementia refers to a group of dementia that involve degeneration in one or both of the frontal or temporal lobes of the brain. The most common form of FTD is Pick's disease, a rare disorder that causes damage to brain cells in the frontal and temporal lobes. Pick's disease affects the individual's personality significantly, usually resulting in a decline in social skills, coupled with emotional apathy. Unlike other types of dementia, Pick's disease typically results in behavior and personality changes manifesting before memory loss and speech problems. About 50% of people with FTD have a family history of the disease.

Parkinson's Disease-Related Dementia

Parkinson's disease is a chronic, progressive neurological condition characterized by movement problems and tremors. In its advanced stages, the disease can also affect cognitive functioning. As many as 65% of people suffering from Parkinson's disease will go on to develop symptoms of dementia as the disease progresses. Similar to dementia with Lewy bodies, the formation of abnormal protein deposits in nerve cells affects normal brain activity. Common cognitive symptoms include experiencing difficulties in reasoning, recall, speech, and judgment.

> **AGELESS MIND FACT**
>
> An estimated 10 million people worldwide live with Parkinson's disease - over 1 million of them in the U.S.

Alcohol-Related Dementia

Alcohol-induced dementia is the result of brain damage due to a long-term history of excessive drinking. Nutrition problems, which often accompany long-time alcohol abuse, can be another contributing factor, since parts of the brain may be damaged by vitamin deficiencies. Physicians often overlook alcohol-related dementia because they may not recognize their patients' alcohol abuse problems. Alcohol-induced dementia causes patients to develop memory problems and is associated with language impairment, learning difficulties, and trouble with complex motor task functioning.

Huntington's Disease-Related Dementia

Huntington's disease is an inherited degenerative brain disease that affects the mind and body. It usually appears between the ages of 30 and 50 and is characterized by intellectual decline and irregular involuntary movement of the limbs or facial muscles. Dementia occurs in the majority of Huntington's cases. Other symptoms include personality change, memory disturbance, slurred speech, impaired judgment, and psychiatric problems. Delusions and hallucinations may also occur. There is currently no treatment available to stop the progression of the disease, but medication can control movement disorders and psychiatric symptoms.

Mixed Dementia

Sometimes dementia is caused by more than one medical condition. This is called mixed dementia. The most common form of mixed dementia results from a combination of both Alzheimer's and vascular disease.

When is it Just Old Age... Or Something More?

Not all memory loss is a sign of Alzheimer's disease or dementia. It is important to realize that most memory lapses after fifty are normal and harmless. The term coined for this benign forgetfulness is *age-associated memory impairment*. Forgetting where you parked the car at the mall or your grandchild's first name may just be old age, but forgetting that you have been to the mall or that you have a grandchild is more serious. In the early stages, such lapses may be subtle, and a person can cover for these changes. Every case of dementia, however, reaches a point when it can no longer be confused with age. The following table summarizes the differences between the two.

Normal Aging vs. Alzheimer's / Dementia

Ability	Normal Aging	Alzheimer's / Dementia
Independent living skills (Driving, shopping, paying bills)	No trouble	Impaired early - worsens as disease progresses
Personal care activities (Dressing, grooming, bathing)	No trouble	Impaired - gradually worsens as disease progresses
Able to learn new skills	A bit slower	Unable to learn new skills
Social skills	No trouble	Lost as disease progresses
Orientation	Does not get lost often Understands days & dates	Gets lost easily and has trouble distinguishing days & dates
Complaints of memory loss	Frequently forgets names, words, & numbers	Has no awareness of memory loss

Alzheimer's and Your Ageless Mind

Alzheimer's disease is one of many age-related diseases that so far has no cure to eradicate the underlying cause. Like some cancers, diabetes, high cholesterol, and hypertension, it begins in middle age or later, worsens with time, and if left untreated, significantly diminishes one's longevity and quality of life.

While at this very moment scientists are scrambling to develop effective Alzheimer's drugs, the most promising path is through prevention – protecting a healthy brain rather than trying to reverse damage that has already occurred. Considerable evidence points to lifestyle as the key to defending our brains from Alzheimer's disease. Diet, mental and physical exercise, stress reduction, social engagement – these and other strategies not only improve cognitive performance quickly, but they may also delay the onset of dementia for many people. Until a drug cure can be fully realized, these lifestyle strategies may provide the surest way to improve your memory, strengthen cognitive ability, and protect your ageless mind.

Memory

" *No memory is ever alone; it's at the end of a trail of memories, a dozen trails that each have their own associations.* "

Louis L'Amour

WHAT IS MEMORY?

Memory defines who we are. Without our memories we have no past, cannot plan for the future, and have no context for appreciating the present.

Memory consists of two major components: getting information into our brains, also known as **encoding**, and retrieving that information later, or **recall**. Forming new memories and recalling them later involves a complex array of biochemical events, electrical transmissions, and neural connections that occur throughout the brain.

Three Stages of Memory

While several different models of memory have been proposed, the "stage model" of memory is often used to explain the basic structure and function of memory. Initially proposed in 1968 by Atkinson and Shiffrin, this theory outlines three separate stages of memory: sensory memory, short-term memory, and long-term memory.

Sensory Memory

From moment to moment, our brains are bombarded with millions of little messages. We observe, hear, smell, taste, and feel a multitude of stimuli from the outside world. At the same time, we are also responding to internal cues – various thoughts, emotions, and sensations - that help qualify these stimuli. From this, our brain and nervous system create a very brief "snapshot" of this activity that we call **sensory memory**. A sensory memory could be seeing a traffic light turn green, hearing a bird chirp, or feeling that the shower water is too cold. Sensory memory typically is held for no more than a second or two.

Short-Term Memory

With so many sensory memories being recognized by your body at once, your brain would become quickly overwhelmed if it were to focus upon all of them. In response to this data burden, the brain is forced to pick and choose what to acknowledge as noteworthy. Our brains are designed to instinctively pluck out the important information and retain it in what we call ***short-term memory***. This short-term memory, also known as "working memory," allows us to carry out quick tasks, like responding to an email or hearing a phone number from directory assistance and remembering it just long enough to dial it. Working memory stores information for a very brief period, generally from 1 to 18 seconds.

Long-Term Memory

If we want to retain information for more than just a few moments, our brains have to push it through to ***long-term memory***. Only a few sensory memories make it to short-term memory, and even fewer memories are stored as long-term ones. We have two kinds of long-term memory: declarative and procedural. ***Declarative memory*** is the memory of ideas or events. ***Procedural memory*** is remembering how one can do things. The words themselves help us remember which is which; declarative memory makes it possible to express something, or "declare." Procedural memory helps us to do something - to "proceed."

How Memories are Formed in the Brain

How the brain creates a memory has long been the subject of speculation and study. While it had been difficult to research how a living brain operates, the development of modern imaging tools along with studies of non-human subjects have provided great insight.

Memory is a function of your brain and nervous system, consisting of billions of nerve cells or ***neurons***. In this complex electrical system the neurons act as the wiring. Each neuron communicates with thousands of others, each separated by a tiny gap called a ***synapse***. When a new memory is being formed, data is moved from one neuron to another, crossing over the tiny gaps with the help of a chemical called a ***neurotransmitter***.

Each of these neurons has a specialty. Some handle information from the senses. Others deal with thoughts, feelings, and actions. As each bit of data is collected, it is turned into an electrical impulse and transmitted from cell to cell until it reaches the appropriate brain center.

For example, when eating a chocolate chip cookie, you experience it with all of your senses. Since each neuron carries just one unique bit of information, all the unique qualities registered by each of the senses will be handled by different neurons:

How Neurons Record a Chocolate Chip Cookie

Sense Neurons	Recorded Information
Vision Neurons	The cookie's shape, size, color
Taste Neurons	Sweetness
Smell Neurons	Brown sugar, chocolate
Touch Neurons	Hardness, warmth
Hearing Neurons	Crunch

Once the data is collected by neurons and sent to the brain centers, they become memory traces. This information from the senses, along with your thoughts, feelings, and actions, is then consolidated in the brain. This involves putting together all the bits of new information and then relating it to the brain's existing information, thus creating a context and location for its newly formed memory.

Why We Forget

No one can remember everything. An essential part of the memory process is making decisions about what information is valuable to you and worth the effort to encode. Most people feel very frustrated and even embarrassed when they have to say, "I've forgotten." But the act of forgetting is a natural part of the process. Imagine if you remembered every detail of every minute or every hour of every day during your entire life, no matter how good, bad, or insignificant. Now imagine trying to sift through all of it for the important stuff... like where you left your keys.

There are many reasons why we forget things and often these reasons overlap. Sometimes information just never makes it to our long-term memory. Other times, the information gets there, but is lost before it can be properly stored. Other reasons include decay, which means that information that is not used for an extended period decays or fades away over time. It is even possible that our brains are pre-programmed to eventually erase data that no longer appears pertinent to us.

How Much Forgetting is Too Much?

Consider the forgetfulness that many people experience as they age. A man comes home, flips his keys on the counter, and then can't find them five minutes later. A woman misplaces her reading glasses or her checkbook. She can't come up with the name of a coworker in the elevator. Three floors later, it comes to her.

This kind of incidental forgetfulness isn't too serious. Age-related memory changes are very common and are most often not related to a disease process. As we get older, we have to pay more attention or focus more on certain activities. It gets more difficult, for example, to drive and talk on the phone at the same time, because neither activity is getting your full attention.

On the other hand, if a person finds that he or she still cannot remember an experience even when focusing upon it, then that may be a sign of concern. If he or she frequently forgets things that used to be fairly easy to remember, it may be a red flag. As Dr. Barry Gordon of the Johns Hopkins

> ### AGELESS MIND FACT
> Memory techniques such as "brain training" have been proven to help memory loss.

Memory Clinic puts it: "Miss an exit on the highway once - that happens. Miss it five times and that's another story."

The key question is whether behavior has become different from usual. If these changes in cognitive ability are impacting the quality and function of day-to-day life, then the cause of concern may be well-founded. While all of us have our moments of forgetfullness, memory impairment that could potentianlly put us in harm's way should be taken seriously.

Mild Cognitive Impairment

As part of the explosion of research into Alzheimer's disease over the last decade, scientists have become more aware of the differences between typical age-related memory lapses and a more serious condition called ***mild cognitive impairment***. People with mild cognitive impairment may be more forgetful than usual, but can still pay the bills and handle most daily tasks. Symptoms include losing track of a conversation, having difficulty remembering details from a TV show they've just watched, or consistently forgetting appointments.

"These people are starting to forget important information that they used to remember regularly, like doctor appointments or meeting friends," says Dr. Ron Petersen, a member of the Alzheimer's Association's medical and scientific advisory council.

Alzheimer's is thought to be the underlying cause of most mild cognitive impairment. Research indicates, however, that not everyone who experiences impairment develops dementia or its worsening symptoms.

Strengthening Your Memory

While forgetting some information is a natural part of being human, there are proven ways to strengthen your overall memory as you age. The following are some strategies that will help you to improve your memory throughout your life.

- **Maintain a positive attitude about your memory.** If you ask any elementary school teacher what children forget in the classroom every day, you'll learn that in addition to forgetting facts, they also leave behind books, bags, gym shoes, lunchboxes, and even winter coats in the middle of January. When the teacher reminds a fifth grader that he left his baseball cap in the coatroom, she doesn't hear, "What's the matter with me... it must be another junior moment!" But by middle age, many people begin to focus on any fault in memory as evidence for its demise. When it comes to aging, attitude is everything. With a positive attitude, proper nutrition, and exercise, your memory can improve every year of your life.

- **Focus your full attention on remembering.** If you haven't registered something in your mind, then it is, of course, quite difficult to recall it. When people believe their memory is fading, they don't bother trying to concentrate on registering new information, thus fulfilling their negative expectation. Many people complain, for example, that they can't remember names, but usually they don't focus enough to register the name in the first place. Mobilizing and focusing your attention are two of the simplest secrets to strengthening memory.

- **Take advantage of your preferred learning style.** Visual types learn best by reading or otherwise seeing what they want to remember. Auditory learners prefer listening. They will remember the content of a book much better if they listen to it on tape or read it aloud. Individuals with a more kinesthetic learning style are more hands-on – they learn and remember best when they are moving and physically interacting rather than sitting passively at a desk. One of the simplest ways to strengthen your recall is to learn things in your preferred mode.

- **Connect new information to something you already know.** Recall works best by association. The more associations you create, the easier it is to remember. For example, if you want to remember someone's name, find our where he lives and what he does, then make connections in your mind with other people from the same area and/or profession.

Using Your Senses to Enhance Memory

Your five senses of sight, touch, taste, hearing, and smell work together to contribute to an elaborate profile of a memory. The more senses that can be included in your memory, the more neuro-pathways will be created to encode the information.

Sight

Sight is the strongest sense for creating mental pictures. Create an image in your mind's eye. For example, if you wish to remember the words "dog" and "bicycle" together, you might create an image of a dog riding a bicycle.

Make the images vivid and specific. What breed of dog? What color bicycle? A black Labrador retriever riding a shiny, red bicycle is easier to remember than a generic dog and bicycle.

Touch

The skin is the largest organ in the human body, and touch is the sense that resides there. Whether it comes through the hands or feet or face, people get lots of data from the tactile properties of the environment and the objects within it.

Taste

There are about 10,000 taste buds in the human mouth, and each taste bud contains roughly 50 taste cells that communicate data to our brains.

AGELESS MIND FACT

Scent is a very powerful and underestimated sense. It is closely related to emotions.

Hearing

Sounds are caused by vibrations of varying pitch, quality, and loudness - each with a unique pattern.

Smell

Scent is linked to the hippocampus and emotional memory. There are about 5 million receptor cells in the human nose, and it is only a short trip from there to the brain where smells are stored in our long-term memory. Anyone who has encountered a smell that brought back memories knows how closely smell is to memory. In fact, scientists have found that if you associate a list of words with smells, you will better remember the words.

Putting it All Together

By focusing on your senses to help encode memories, from remembering how something smelled or felt to creating vivid images in your mind's eye, you'll discover that some information will become almost impossible to forget. Great memory uses the entire mind and all of your senses. This sensory focus will help make your memories last longer over time with more neural pathways being used and strengthened. Once you realize that you can improve your memory throughout life with this simple awareness, you'll discover a more comfortable approach toward learning anything.

Memory and Your Ageless Mind

Upon reaching middle age, many people start to notice that their memory is slipping a bit. This is particularly true when they are tired or under stress. Naturally, they get worried that more serious troubles lie ahead. While a certain amount of memory trouble is a normal part of aging, it is comforting to know that even into our nineties, about one-third of both men and women experience no significant memory loss at all.

The rest of us, however, can expect some change in memory function. While not limiting in healthy adults, these changes can still be troubling to the individual experiencing them. These changes include taking longer to learn new things and having trouble remembering names and strings of numbers.

There are, however, also memory advantages for the aging brain. The right and left hemispheres of the brain begin to communicate better as the brain ages. In children and young adults, these two sides of the brain work more independently. Studies show that older individuals demonstrate improved mental abilities when both sides of the brain work together. Experiencing improved language skills is just one of the ways that this helps us as we age.

It is important as we grow older to retain a positive attitude about our brains and memory. Through exercise, nutrition, and memory training, it is possible to have an overall improved memory even while facing minor loss along the way. It is through these and other strategies that you will be able to retain a strong, young, and healthy mind.

CHAPTER THREE

Brain Safety

*" Protect your brain... after all,
it's the only one you have. "*

Dr. Mehmet Oz

PROTECTING THE BRAIN FROM INJURY

Each year in the United States, 1.7 million people suffer a traumatic brain injury. According to the Centers for Disease Control, these brain injuries are a contributing factor in 30% of all injury-related deaths.

The brain is protected by the skull where it floats around surrounded by cerebrospinal fluid. This fluid helps cushion the brain and protects it from minor shock. If your head moves too quickly, however, your brain will move through the fluid and hit the sides of your skull, causing a hemorrhage.

A brain injury consists of both primary and secondary events. Primary brain events, including fractures, bruises, blood clots, and lacerations, are more or less complete at the time of impact. A secondary cycle of biochemical events is set in motion by the trauma and is the major contributor to long-term deficits associated with brain injury.

The best way to protect ourselves from the long-term consequences of traumatic brain injury is through prevention. Here are some simple ways to protect your most vital organ.

Be Safe In and Around Cars

When purchasing a vehicle, choose one that has met high safety standards and is well ranked in protecting against high-impact collisions. Make it a habit to wear your seat belt, both as a driver and as a passenger. Avoid using cell phones when driving – either for calls or texting; according to recent studies, you may be four times more likely to have an accident when you do. Even when using a headset, you can be as distracted as if you were over the legal blood-alcohol limit.

As a pedestrian, be careful walking through busy parking lots and remember to cross the road at a marked crossing whenever possible. If you're out for a walk or run on the open road, make sure to wear bright, reflective clothing, especially after dark. Remember that some drivers may be distracted and not paying proper attention. Keep a cautious eye on the traffic and be aware of your surroundings at all times.

Wear a Helmet

Traumatic head injuries are the leading cause of death from recreational activities including skating, skiing, horseback riding, and bicycling. In the United States alone, approximately 900 persons die from head injuries due to bicycle crashes every year. According to the National Traffic Safety Administration, helmets are 85 to 88% effective in preventing head injuries. Whether you participate in a contact sport or are simply going out for some skating in the park, avoid becoming a statistic by protecting your head.

Helmets should fit directly over your forehead and have tight chin-straps. If your helmet hits a hard surface – in an accident or if you drop it down the stairs – it can lose its ability to absorb a hard blow. That's when it may be time for a new one. Keep this in mind when borrowing or purchasing a used helmet.

Injury-Proof Your Home

Take precautions to protect your brain at home. Try the following tips to prevent accidents and injuries in your own backyard.

Protecting Your Brain at Home

Accidents in the home rank among the leading causes of injury and death in the United States. The following tips can help avoid falls around the house:

1. Improve lighting throughout the home.

2. Install handrails on both sides of stairs.

3. Be safe in the bathroom. Use nonslip mats on the bathtub and shower floors; install grab bars next to the toilet and in the tub or shower.

4. Remove tripping hazards such as loose rugs, electrical cords, and clutter in walkways.

5. Stay upright in the rain and snow. Skid-proof the stairs, carry fewer items during wet weather, and treat icy areas with salt as needed.

Head Injuries and Alzheimer's Disease

It may be obvious that banging your head in a car crash or bad fall can seriously harm your brain. What is lesser known, however, is that traumatic brain injury has been linked to an increased risk of Alzheimer's disease.

The link between head injuries and Alzheimer's disease is examined in the MIRAGE study (Multi-Institutional Research in Alzheimer Genetic Epidemiology). According to the research, patients with Alzheimer's were nearly ten times more likely to have had a prior head injury that resulted in loss of consciousness. The study states that "head injury with loss of consciousness and, to a lesser extent, head injury without loss of consciousness, increased the risk of Alzheimer's disease." Researchers at Duke University and the National Institute on Aging additionally suggest that the more severe the head injury, the greater the risk of developing the disease.

Evidence of Plaques and Tangles

Further research conducted by Dr. Douglas H. Smith at the University of Pennsylvania supports previous links between a single episode of brain trauma and the development of Alzheimer's later in life. In animal studies, scientists induced brain trauma without direct impact, similar to what humans often experience in automobile accidents. Analysis of damaged brain cells showed extensive amyloid plaques and tau tangle accumulation – the same as found in Alzheimer's disease. These changes were evident as early as 3 to 10 days after the injury.

> **AGELESS MIND FACT**
>
> Former NFL football players between the ages of 30 and 49 have 19 times the rate of Alzheimer's compared to non-players of the same age.

Still, what may be obvious to brain researchers is not widely known by the public, warns Samuel Gandy, MD, an Alzheimer's disease research professor at Mount Sinai School of Medicine; multiple concussions dramatically increase the risk of neurological degeneration years later. Most recently, a Columbia University analysis confirmed that Alzheimer's disease was nearly four times more common in elderly people who severely injured their heads in accidental falls.

PROTECTING YOUR BRAIN FROM TOXINS

Toxic exposure, like physical injury, hurts the brain. Many substances have the potential to be toxic to the brain, but most people simply are not aware of the risks. From daily exposure of heavy metals to consuming harmful chemicals in our food, both naturally occurring and man-made toxins can threaten your ageless mind. Understanding the sources of some of these brain poisons can help you avoid them.

Mercury

Mercury, a silvery liquid metal at room temperature, was first identified as a human toxin in 1866 when two laboratory technicians who worked with the metal died from poisoning. It was not until 1956, however, after a mercury poisoning occurred in Japan that mercury became widely recognized as a dangerous toxin. The source of the mercury contamination was pollution from a chemical manufacturing plant that had polluted the water supply.

Methylmercury is the organic, more toxic form of mercury. Symptoms of methylmercury poisoning include confusion, depression, fatigue, and memory loss. Mercury does its dirty work by promoting free radical production and inflammation - the same process that causes normal brain degeneration, but mercury does it much faster. Most human exposure comes from fish consumption and dental fillings.

Fish

Mercury occurs naturally in the environment as well as being released into the air through industrial pollution. Once released, it falls back with rain into waterways (lakes, rivers, streams, oceans) where bacteria convert it into methylmercury, its organic form. Fish absorb the methylmercury as they feed in these waters, building up the toxin in their systems over time. This is why larger fish that have lived the longest have among the highest levels.

These large fish include swordfish, shark, king mackerel, and tilefish. By comparison, smaller fish, as well as most shellfish, have among the lowest levels of mercury. As consumers of fish, we need to be careful about avoiding high levels of mercury. The problem is that mercury lingers in our bodies and, over time, can damage nerve cells. The following chart shows some of the safest fish, as well as the ones to avoid.

Mercury Levels in Fish Measured in Parts Per Million

Lowest Mercury Levels	Highest Mercury Levels
Salmon - .014	Tilefish - 1.45
Crawfish - .033	Shark - .988
Anchovies - .043	Swordfish - .976
Catfish - .049	Bowfin - .960
Flounder / Sole - .060	King Mackerel - .730
Whitefish - .069	Orange Roughy - .554
Trout (freshwater) - .072	Marlin - .485
Cod - .095	Grouper - .465
Trout (rainbow) - .110	Bass (large mouth) - .430
Tuna (canned light) - .118	Walleye - .400

Source: US Environmental Protection Agency

Dental

Eating fish is not the only way that mercury gets into our bodies. Your mouth may be filled with mercury. About 80% of all American adults have mercury amalgam, so-called "silver" fillings, in their teeth. Does this mercury pose a risk to our health? The American Dental Association has said that once mercury is sealed in an amalgam, it is locked in and cannot escape. Scientific studies have shown, however, that a significant amount of mercury vapor does escape from fillings and is absorbed by the body. Chewing, consuming hot foods, even brushing your teeth causes mercury to be released from amalgam fillings.

There has been debate as to whether or not these mercury vapors are significant enough to be harmful. While many dentists have since switched to alternative fillings, the Food and Drug Administration provides this statement:

Dental amalgam releases low levels of mercury vapor that can be inhaled. High levels of mercury vapor exposure are associated with adverse effects in the brain and the kidneys. FDA has reviewed the best available scientific evidence to determine whether the low levels of mercury vapor associated with dental amalgam fillings are a cause for concern. Based on this evidence, FDA considers dental amalgam fillings safe for adults and children ages 6 and above.

Accumulative Effects

Many of us are walking around with mercury levels in excess of what is considered to be safe. A study conducted by a physician in San Francisco found that 16% of those tested had mercury levels significantly higher than what the EPA deemed as safe. Having elevated levels of mercury doesn't mean that you're suffering from mercury poisoning, but it does mean that the toxic load on your body is higher than it should be and that it will be less able to defend itself properly against free radicals. If your body is constantly challenged with a high toxic load, your memory, concentration, and cognitive agility can suffer.

> **HEALTHY BRAIN TIP**
> Looking for natural ways to remove mercury from your system? Eat garlic. Garlic binds to mercury and helps remove it from the body.

Lead

Lead is a neurotoxin that is particularly harmful to children but also affects mental performance in adults. Acute lead exposure is a well-documented cause of brain and nervous system damage and has been linked to learning disabilities and mental retardation in young children. It is likely that even at low levels this toxic metal produces harmful effects. Although there has been an effort to raise awareness about the dangers of lead and public campaigns to have it removed from apartment buildings and private homes, lead toxicity is still a problem. Environmental sources of lead include:

Lead Paint

About 40% of the homes built before 1978 contain lead paint, and very often it has been painted over with other paint. Nevertheless, any lead residue can cause problems. Paint can peel and chip off the walls and can be eaten by curious toddlers. Microscopic lead dust particles can be inhaled by both children and adults. Easy at-home test kits are available to help you determine whether your walls contain lead residue. If you find that you have lead paint in your home, it's best to hire a professional to remove it from the walls so that lead dust particles don't spread throughout your house.

Older Plumbing

Although banned in new construction, lead or lead-lined pipes are still present in older homes, and the lead in them can leach into the water. Homes with plumbing that dates back before 1930 most likely have lead pipes. If possible, replace lead pipes with copper or plastic. If not, don't use the tap water for drinking. A water purification system may help the problem, but have the water tested (by a local water company) to be sure it is safe to drink.

Decorative Dishware

Ceramic and earthenware containers, especially those imported from other countries, may be decorated with colorful lead-based glazes and paint. Lead from the dish can leach into food or drink. These dishes are fine for display, but unless the dish says it is lead-free, consider not eating from it.

Aluminum

Aluminum is the most abundant metal found on the planet. It is found naturally in food, soil, water, and even the air we breathe. It is also in a wide variety of consumer products, from antacids to deodorants to processed foods to cookware. Our bodies can handle a limited amount of aluminum and can excrete small amounts. While daily ingestion of about 20 milligrams of aluminum poses no health risk, modern-day consumption typically exceeds what many experts believe to be safe. For example, many brands of antacids contain as much as 200 milligrams in a single tablet. If you routinely use antacids, you could be ingesting up to 4 grams of aluminum daily.

What's wrong with consuming so much aluminum? Aluminum consumption may increase your risk for neurological disease. There is an abnormally high accumulation of aluminum in the brains of Alzheimer's patients; up to 30 times more than the normal level. There has been a dispute in the scientific community as to whether this accumulation of aluminum in the brain is the cause of Alzheimer's or merely a result of the disease. Regardless of the answer, it may be wise to limit your use of aluminum-based products, especially considering that high amounts of aluminum have negative health effects. Here are some common ways that we consume aluminum.

Personal Hygiene Products

Deodorants, especially antiperspirants, use aluminum as an active agent. There are several aluminum-free deodorants on the market, including those that contain baking soda. These can be easily found in health food stores and online. Some brands of shampoo, especially anti-dandruff shampoo, also contain aluminum. Read the package label carefully for aluminum content.

> **HEALTHY BRAIN TIP**
> Try an alternative to cooking with aluminum foil. Parchment paper can be used for lining pans and baking.

Medications

Antacids can contain 200 milligrams or more of aluminum in a single tablet. If you use antacids frequently (more than once or twice a month) try switching to brands that contain calcium carbonate and avoid those products that contain aluminum hydroxide. Aluminum can also be found in popular over-the-counter and prescription pain-killers and anti-diarrhea medicines.

Processed Food

Aluminum is added as an emulsifying agent in many foods, including processed cheese (especially those that are single-sliced). It is also found in many cake mixes, self-rising flour, prepared dough, and nondairy creamers.

Chemicals and Food

Modern production methods have introduced new environmental toxins that plague our food supply on a daily basis. It's not just the food itself that we have to watch, but all the storage containers as well. Among these new threats to our brain health our two common culprits: BPA and pesticides.

BPA

BPA (bisphenol A) is a synthetic substance used to create polycarbonate plastics, widely used in such products as water bottles, packaging, and food storage containers. Research shows that it can leach into food and drinks, and that we are widely exposed to low, but continuous, levels. Most of the studies have been done on animals – usually rats – so researchers can't say for sure that the effects are the same in humans. A 2008 study by Yale University researchers found, however, that administering BPA to monkeys at a daily dose equal to the current U.S. Environmental Protection Agency's reference safe daily limit (50 micrograms per kilogram of body weight) interfered with synapse formation in the hippocampus and prefrontal cortex, two areas of the brain critical for cognition, attention, and memory.

> **HEALTHY BRAIN TIP**
> When possible, avoid plastic products with recycling label #7 on them. These are more likely to contain BPA.

In the face of growing evidence, experts agree that it is best to avoid BPA as much as possible to preserve brain health and function as we age. Many manufacturers are phasing out BPA – most notably makers of baby bottles and water bottles – and will often state on the label that a product is "BPA-free." You can reduce your exposure by using metal, glass, or ceramic food storage containers. When using plastic containers, avoid putting them in the microwave or cleaning them in the dishwasher, as BPA reacts to the heat.

Pesticides

Chemical pesticides used to kill pests on fruits and vegetables can be harmful to humans over time. While they are designed to be safe in small doses, the residue gets stored in our fat cells and can stay in the body indefinitely.

Over time, levels build up and can raise the risk of Parkinson's and other neurological diseases. A 2008 study in the journal *Chemico-Biological Interactions* noted that ongoing low-dose exposure to organophosphorus pesticides (the kind most commonly used in the U.S.) results in cognitive impairment. Pesticides can also age the brain by triggering inflammation and increasing damaging free radicals. Anything that accelerates that process is going to have a direct effect on how well your brain functions today, as well as your ability to maintain good brain health for years to come.

To limit contact, avoid using pesticides in and around your home and eat organic food whenever possible. If you don't have access to or can't afford organic produce, at least be sure to fully wash all fruits and vegetables before consuming.

Bug Repellent

Insecticides prevent bug bites and protect us from serious illnesses like Lyme disease and West Nile Virus, but there are some questions about the safety of some of these chemicals. For example, the chemically engineered active ingredient N,N-Diethyl-meta-toluamide, or "DEET," has been linked to brain and nerve damage.

A new study by the University of Texas Southwestern Medical Center, published in the *Journal of Neurochemistry*, found that DEET-based mosquito repellents "interfere with proper nerve signals, disrupt the hormone dopamine needed for healthy brain function, and invoke chemical mechanisms associated with neurological disorders and nerve degeneration."

Earlier studies have also linked DEET to brain damage. Duke University researchers found that the toxin is associated with brain cell damage, harmful interactions with some medications, and behavioral changes. Scientists in the lab observed brain cell death and behavioral changes in animals exposed to DEET after frequent and prolonged use.

DEET products claim to be safe when "used as directed," but according to the chemical industry's own material safety data sheets, its toxic effects include reproductive disturbances, genetic material mutations, and central nervous system disorders.

Alternative Strategies

Mosquitoes can be controlled without declaring chemical warfare. Be vigilant about not allowing pools of water to gather in the backyard where mosquitoes can lay their eggs. Cover up when you go outdoors; wear long sleeves and long pants and shoes with socks in areas that are infested with mosquitoes. Don't wear perfume or aftershave that can attract insects.

Instead of spraying yourself or your family members with DEET-based mosquito repellents, try using a natural bug repellent such as Bite Blocker®, a soy-based insecticide, or Burt's Bees Herbal Insect Repellent®. Any repellent containing citronella is also a good choice. Oil of citronella repels mosquitoes and is harmless to humans. When used as directed, it works for 2 hours before needing to be reapplied.

If you find that natural insect repellents do not work for you, then use a DEET product sparingly, focusing the spray more on your clothing than on your skin.

Brain Safety and Your Ageless mind

Protecting your brain is a critical component of optimum brain fitness. Damage can occur in a variety of ways including obvious ones like accidents and brain trauma.

Environmental toxins such as lead and pesticides can also cause trouble for your brain, creating free radicals, increasing brain-aging inflammation, or worse. Your body has an efficient detoxification system that can eliminate many of the toxic health threats you face every day. Since experts aren't sure how continued, low-level exposure to these environmental chemicals interact with each other to affect us long-term, it makes sense to reduce exposure whenever possible.

Stay vigilant in the protection of your healthy brain. Remember that you are the primary caretaker of your own ageless mind.

CHAPTER FOUR

Sleep

" A well spent day brings
happy sleep. "

Leonard da Vinci

SLEEP AND THE BRAIN

Good sleep is essential for optimal brain health. It gives brain cells a chance to repair themselves and activates neural connections that might otherwise deteriorate due to inactivity. The sleeping brain consolidates emotional and social experiences, forms new synaptic connections, and stores memories. Robert Stickgold, PhD, of the Division of Sleep Medicine at Harvard Medical School notes, "The fundamental purpose of sleep is to catch up on processing the information received during the waking hours."

Over the years, researchers have conducted numerous tests to examine how sleep affects our ability to absorb new information. In a well-known 2002 Harvard study, students learned to type a number sequence as quickly as possible. After a good night's sleep, they repeated the task and showed improvement in accuracy and speed. "The brain seems to take advantage of sleep to recognize and store what we did during the day," says Maria Bautista, a sleep disorder specialist at Georgetown University Hospital in Washington, D.C.

Sleep as Preventative Medicine

Besides being essential for an ageless mind, sleep provides preventative medicine, rejuvenating all the cells in the body and protecting our systems against malfunction. Some of the benefits of restorative sleep include:

Cardiovascular Health

Getting sufficient sleep helps lower high blood pressure and reduces inflammation, helping the body prevent heart disease, coronary artery disease, hypertension, and stroke. Researchers at the University of Chicago report that too little sleep can also promote calcium buildup in the heart arteries, leading to the plaques that can then break apart and cause heart attacks and strokes. According to Diane Lauderdale, PhD, each additional hour of sleep is associated with a 33% reduced risk of the artery calcification that leads to coronary heart disease.

Positive Mood

Sleep deprivation has been linked to mood problems and depression in a number of scientific studies. One study published in the journal *Sleep* found that sleep problems were an early sign of depression and that treatment of sleep issues may protect some individuals from developing the disorder.

Strengthened Immunity

A regular sleep schedule will help strengthen the immune system, protecting the body against colds and infections. Researchers found that people in a sleep study who stayed awake for seventy-two consecutive hours experienced a significant drop in white cell production. In another study, adults who had been given a flu shot after four nights of reduced sleep had less than half of the antibody response 10 days later compared with individuals having had normal sleep.

Maintain a Healthy Weight

Quality sleep allows the body to maintain a stable and healthy body weight. In a 2004 study, Stanford School of Medicine researchers found that sleep loss leads to higher levels of a hormone that triggers appetite, and lower levels of a hormone that tells the body it's full. The findings add to the growing evidence showing that sleep duration may be an important regulator of body weight and metabolism.

Stress and Anxiety

Good sleep increases our ability to deal with stress and helps to reduce anxiety. Research indicates that chronic sleep problems may make you more vulnerable to the development of anxiety disorders.

Safe Driving

A well-rested night makes you less susceptible to accidents. Sleep sharpens alertness and powers of attention. According to the National Highway Traffic Safety Administration (NHTSA), drowsiness is responsible for more than 100,000 traffic accidents each year, causing 40,000 injuries and 1,550 deaths. Fatigue has also played a role in many airplane, train, and boating crashes, some of them with devastating consequences.

How Much Sleep Do We Need?

Many people simply aren't getting the sleep they need. According to the National Institutes of Health, the average adult gets only six hours and forty minutes of sleep each night, and just slightly more on the weekends. In today's fast-paced society, 6 or 7 hours of sleep may seem like a great achievement. In reality, it's a recipe for chronic sleep deprivation.

Age	Sleep Needs
Newborns (0-2 months)	12-18 hours
Infants (3-11 months)	14-15 hours
Toddlers (1-3 years)	12-14 hours
Preschoolers (3-5 years)	11-13 hours
Younger children (5-10 years)	10-11 hours
Older children (10-17 years)	8.5-9.25 hours
Adults	7-9 hours
Older Adults	7-9 hours

Source: National Sleep Foundation

Different People, Different Needs

While sleep requirements vary slightly from person to person, most healthy adults need between 7 to 9 hours of sleep per night to function at their best. Children and teens need even more. Despite the notion that sleep needs decrease with age, most older adults still need at least 7.5 to 8 hours of sleep. But how much sleep is enough for you? At the end of the day, a good night's sleep is one that leaves you feeling well rested and able to function at your best.

Common Sleep Inhibitors

Quality sleep is critical for a well-functioning brain. Unfortunately, as we age, more than half of us experience sleep problems, potentially compromising both our mental and physical health.

While chronic sleep problems affect millions of us, temporary sleep issues are more common and will affect nearly everyone in his or her lifetime. Here are some of the many things that can lead to sleep trouble:

- **Medicines** including some asthma medications, antihistamines, cough medicines, and anticonvulsants disturb sleep.

- **Caffeine** from coffee, tea, chocolate, cola, and some herbs can disturb sleep, especially when consumed later in the day or at night.

- **Alcohol, nicotine, and marijuana** can initially induce sleepiness, but have the reverse effect as they wear off, often causing you to wake up several hours after going to sleep.

- **Women's health issues** like pregnancy, PMS, and menopause can cause fluctuations in hormone levels that can disrupt the sleep cycle.

- **Chronic pain** leads to sleep deprivation, which can increase the sensation of pain, which in turn creates more sleeplessness.

- **Psychiatric conditions** such as obsessive-compulsive disorder, depression, anxiety, or dementia can cause sleep problems.

- **Gastrointestinal problems** such as reflux or overeating can create disruptive sleep.

- **Stress** of all types can cause temporary sleep loss.

- **Late shift** working and particularly "swing shift" working can wreak havoc with sleep cycles. Long-distance traveling and "jet lag" presents similar problems.

Sleep Disorders

At some point, most of us will have trouble sleeping. If sleep problems are a regular occurrence and interfere with your daily life, you may be suffering from a sleep disorder. Unlike short-term sleep inhibitors, sleep disorders are more serious and are often associated with an underlying medical problem.

Sleep disorders cause more than just sleepiness. Poor quality sleep can have a negative impact on your energy, emotional balance, and health. The following are definitions and symptoms of common sleep disorders. If any of these describe you, it may be time to see a doctor.

Insomnia

The most common sleep complaint at any age is insomnia, the inability to sleep during normal resting hours. Insomnia may be characterized by difficulty falling asleep, wakefulness after a period of sleep, or both. Half of all Americans report experiences with insomnia, many significant enough to have their waking activities impaired. Insomnia is often a symptom of another problem, such as stress, anxiety, depression, or an underlying health condition. It can also be caused by lifestyle choices, including medications, lack of exercise, jet lag, or even coffee consumption.

Whatever the cause of your insomnia, be mindful of your sleep habits and use the "sleep strategies" listed later in this chapter. The good news is that most cases of insomnia can be "cured" with lifestyle changes you can make on your own—without relying on sleep specialists or medications. If not, make an appointment to talk it over with your physician.

Sleep Apnea

Sleep apnea is a common sleep disorder in which sufferers repeatedly stop breathing during the night. This is caused by the throat's soft tissues briefly closing the airway to the lungs, the brain failing to signal the body to breathe, or both. These pauses in breathing interrupt sleep, leading to many awakenings each hour. While most people with sleep apnea don't remember these awakenings, they feel the effects in other ways, such as daytime exhaustion, irritability, depression, inattention, and forgetfulness.

Sleep apnea is a serious, and potentially life-threatening, sleep disorder. Several studies have found that people who suffer from sleep apnea have higher rates of automobile accidents, heart disease, stroke, and Alzheimer's disease. Sleep apnea can be successfully treated with Continuous Positive Airway Pressure (CPAP), a mask-like device that delivers a stream of air while sleeping. Losing weight, elevating the head of the bed, and sleeping on your side can also help in cases of mild to moderate sleep apnea.

> **AGELESS MIND FACT**
> Sleep apnea occurs more often in men. Estimates say that 1 in 25 adult males suffer from the disorder.

Sometimes surgery is also recommended to remove tissues from the airway. If you suspect that you or a loved one may have sleep apnea, see a doctor right away.

Narcolepsy

Narcolepsy is a chronic neurological disorder characterized by the brain's inability to control sleep-wake cycles. At various times throughout the day, people with narcolepsy experience irresistible and sudden bouts of sleep which can last from a few seconds to several minutes. Experts believe narcolepsy may be due to a deficiency in the production of a chemical called *hypocretin* by the brain. In addition, researchers have discovered abnormalities in various parts of the brain involved in regulating REM sleep.

While there is no known cure for narcolepsy, most symptoms can be controlled with drug treatment. Sleepiness is treated with amphetamine-like stimulants while the symptoms of abnormal REM sleep are often treated using antidepressant drugs.

Restless Leg Syndrome (RLS)

Restless Leg Syndrome is a neurological disorder characterized by a tingling, aching, itching, or burning sensation in the legs accompanied by an irresistible urge to move them when sitting or lying down. The unpleasant feeling is sometimes described as a "creeping crawling" feeling inside the leg, making it hard to fall asleep and stay asleep. The cause is often unknown, although RLS seems to run in families and can even start in childhood. It may also accompany other conditions including anemia, pregnancy, rheumatoid arthritis, and Parkinson's disease. It can also be a side effect to certain medications.

In mild cases, symptoms of RLS may be relieved by moderate exercise during the day and relaxation techniques prior to sleeping. Some anticonvulsant medications similar to those used by Parkinson's patients have been found to be helpful in severe cases while the avoidance of stimulants like caffeine, alcohol, and nicotine may help reduce the overall symptoms.

Identifying the Problem

In spite of the fact that these and other chronic sleep problems occur more often among older adults, poor sleep is not a natural nor expected part of the aging process. While research suggests that sleep after age sixty does not change much, life can, and changes in your life and health can lead to sleep problems. Just as one consequence of poor health all too often is disordered sleep, the reverse is also true; if a medical illness is resolved, chances are the sleep problems will be, too.

> **HEALTHY BRAIN TIP**
> Use a sleep journal each day to track your symptoms from the night before.

Start today by tracking your symptoms and sleep patterns, then use that information to make healthy changes to your daytime habits and bedtime routine. If these don't solve the problem, you can turn to a doctor or specialist trained in sleep medicine. Together, you can identify the underlying causes of the trouble and find ways to regain your sleep and improve your quality of life.

SLEEP STRATEGIES

Many sleep problems can be solved by making minor adjustments to the way we prepare for sleep. The following suggestions will help you find new ways to get to sleep and stay asleep. Remember that we are all unique individuals, and what works for one person may not work for another. Experiment with different methods to find what works best for you.

Relax

Create a soothing nighttime routine that encourages sleep. Slow your pace and calm your mind. Plan a transition time. Almost everyone needs time to relax and unwind before going to sleep. A relaxing evening bath, gentle stretching or yoga, writing in a journal, or some light reading are just a few ways to ease into a night of restful sleep. Create a ritual that prepares your body for sleep.

> **HEALTHY BRAIN TIP**
>
> Create your own bedtime soundtrack. Listen to music that you can wind down to.

Keep an Eye on Medications

Be certain that your medication is not keeping you up at night. Many medicines act as stimulants, so check to make sure that wakefulness, disturbed sleep, insomnia, or another sleeping problem isn't the result of medication. If you think any of the prescription or over-the-counter medications you are taking might be interfering with your sleep, discuss alternative therapies with your physician.

Caffeine, Alcohol, Nicotine

Whether it's from coffee, cola, or even a chocolate bar, caffeine can keep us awake - avoiding it in the evenings can help us to sleep more soundly. Similarly, smokers should refrain from using tobacco products too close to bedtime. Alcohol, too, can disturb sleep. While it may initially make you feel drowsy, after a few hours it acts as a stimulant, increasing the number of awakenings and generally decreasing the overall quality of sleep. A good plan is to avoid drinking within three hours of bedtime.

Maintain a Sleep Schedule

According to the National Sleep Foundation, the most important sleep strategy is "to maintain a regular sleep and wake pattern seven days a week." Going to bed at the same time each night and waking up at the same time each day, including weekends, will help regulate your internal body clock. Keeping a consistent time for retiring and rising will train your body to expect the same amount of sleep each day.

Prepare Your Bedroom for Sleep

A quiet, dark, and cool environment can help promote good slumber. Insulate the bedroom from outside noise. Soothing nature sounds, calming music, white noise, or even a fan can help. Use heavy curtains, dark shades, or an eye mask to block out light if needed. Keep the temperature comfortably cool and the room well ventilated. And make sure your bedroom is equipped with a comfortable mattress and pillows – keeping in mind that most mattresses wear out after ten years.

Exercise and Physical Activity

Regular exercise is very beneficial for falling asleep and staying asleep. One study by Stanford University of Medicine researchers concluded that people who performed regular, moderately-intense aerobic exercise for 30 to 40 minutes four times a week slept almost an hour longer than those who did not. As well as enjoying better quality sleep, the exercisers were also able to cut the time it took to fall asleep by half. Try to avoid vigorous activity within three hours of bedtime, however. Exercising too late in the evening can energize you and keep you awake.

Food and Drink

Avoid evening liquids. After dinner, try not to drink large quantities of water or other drinks. A full bladder can awaken you during the night, and you may have trouble getting back to sleep. Avoid eating heavy meals at least two to three hours before going to bed. Too much food close to bedtime can lead to difficulty sleeping, but do not go to bed hungry. Feeling hungry can also interfere with your ability to sleep. If you need to, try eating a light snack in the hours before bedtime.

> **HEALTHY BRAIN TIP**
>
> A small cup of warm milk or chamomile tea may help your body relax before bed.

Unplug

Unplug your electronic life. Take computers, video games, and cell phones out of the bedroom, and turn them off an hour or two before bedtime to allow time to "unwind."

Make an effort to put aside the problems and stresses of the day when going to bed. Adopt strategies to reduce your anxiety level. A notebook next to the bed can relieve you from your "Oops, I forgot" thoughts; just write it down in the notebook and forget about it until tomorrow. Keeping your work out of the room will strengthen the mental association between your bedroom and sleep.

Don't Feel Pressured to Sleep

Once in bed, take a few moments to get settled. If you are not asleep after 20 minutes, get up and do something else until you feel tired again. If you awaken in the middle of the night, experience restlessness, and cannot go back to sleep, accept your body's verdict. Don't create the pressure of having to fall asleep. Read for a bit, write in a journal, or listen to an all-night classical radio station. When you feel tired again, go back to bed… and to sleep.

When they occur, sleep problems should not be merely accepted as inevitable. A good night's sleep is an achievable goal for most people given good habits, healthy sleep strategies, and other treatment approaches. Try some of these strategies until you have enough quality sleep to feel alert and well rested. If these tips don't work, see your doctor. You could have a sleep disorder that requires medical attention.

Sleep Medicines

It's the middle of the night, and you're staring at the bedroom ceiling, thinking about work, or bills, or family issues. Sleep just won't come. You look anxiously at the clock again. Even with all of the sleep strategies, if only you could just fall asleep. In these circumstances, it's often tempting to reach for a sleeping pill.

According to the National Sleep Foundation, one in four Americans (and one in three women) takes a sleep aid every year. In 2008 alone, American consumers spent more than four billion dollars on sleep medications.

Sleep aids vary in safety and effectiveness and are rarely meant for more than short-term use. They are safest and most effective as a short-term treatment for situations such as traveling across time zones, recovering from a medical procedure, or when experiencing short-terms bouts of insomnia. If sleeping pills are used over the long term, they are best used "as needed" instead of on a daily basis in order to avoid dependence and tolerance. Working with your healthcare professional is essential to ensure that you get the maximum benefit and can safely monitor potential side effects.

Over-the-Counter (OTC) Sleep Aids

The active ingredient in most over-the-counter (OTC) sleeping aids is *antihistamine*. Antihistamines are generally taken for allergies, hay fever and cold symptoms, in brand name medication such as Benadryl®. As anyone who has taken such allergy medicines knows, antihistamine also has the effect of making you feel sleepy, which is the basis for how these sleep-medicines work. The antihistamines in OTC medicines work to block the chemical histamine in the brain that promotes wakefulness. Some OTC sleep aids combine antihistamines with the pain reliever Acetaminophen (found in brand names like Tylenol PM® and Excedrin PM®). Others, such as NyQuil®, combine antihistamines with alcohol.

OTC sleep aids are meant to be used for short term insomnia only. Sleep experts frequently advise against the use of over-the-counter (OTC) sleep aids because of possible side-effects, questions about their effectiveness, and lack of medical supervision.

Prescription Sleep Medications

Working with your physician to obtain a prescribed and well-monitored sleep aid may be the safest approach for those who require additional sleep help. There are several different types of prescription sleeping pills. In general, the medications act by working on receptors in the brain to slow down the nervous system. Some medications are used more for inducing sleep, while others are used for staying asleep. Some last longer than others in your system and some have a higher risk of becoming habit forming.

Sleep Medicine Caution

While sleep medicine can be effectively used for short-term need, it can't cure the underlying cause of insomnia and can often make the problem worse with long-term use. Here are some concerns about the use of both over-the-counter (OTC) and prescription sleep aids:

1. **Side effects.** Side effects can be severe and include prolonged drowsiness the next day, confusion and forgetfulness, dry mouth, headaches, and nausea. In rare cases, these can include dangerous behaviors such as sleep-walking, sleep-driving, and sleep-eating.

2. **Drug tolerance.** Over time, you may need more of the sleep aid for it to work, which can then lead to more side effects.

3. **Drug dependence.** You may come to rely on sleeping pills to sleep and become unable to sleep (or have worse sleep) without them.

4. **Withdrawal symptoms.** If you stop the medication abruptly, you may have withdrawal symptoms, such as nausea, sweating, and shaking.

5. **Drug interactions.** Sleeping pills can interact with other medications. This can worsen any side effects and be dangerous, especially with prescription painkillers and other sedatives.

6. **Masking an underlying problem.** There may be an underlying medical or mental disorder causing your insomnia that can't be treated with sleep medication.

Consult Your Doctor

Before using sleeping medications of any sort, consult your physician. Some sleep medications can have serious side effects for people with medical problems such as high blood pressure, liver problems, glaucoma, depression, and breathing difficulties. Be sure to follow the instructions carefully and use only at bedtime with eight hours of time dedicated for restful sleep.

Sleep and Your Ageless Mind

As we age, sleep continues to be an important factor for optimal brain health. It strengthens the immune system, improves mood, and sharpens memory and powers of attention.

Over our lifetime, the amount of sleep we need each day declines. While studies show that most adults still require 7-9 hours each night, many older people find it harder to fall asleep and stay asleep. The good news is that researchers have consistently found that poor sleep is not an inevitable part of aging. When insomnia occurs, as it sometimes will, it is generally caused by other factors, many of which can be easily changed on your own or treated with the help of a physician.

Sleep is fundamental to good health, longevity, and an ageless mind. Quality of sleep is linked to quality of life. It is not a luxury for the young; sleep is essential for everyone.

CHAPTER FIVE

Exercise

> *We don't stop playing because we grow old. We grow old because we stop playing.*
>
> **George Bernard Shaw**

EXERCISE AND THE BRAIN

For years we have understood the many health benefits of exercise. Physical activity keeps us in shape, removes excess weight, and helps us to feel young again. How does exercise improve our minds as we age? The secret has to do with oxygen. While the brain consists of only 2% of our body weight, it uses more than 20 percent of its oxygen intake. Oxygen travels to the brain through the blood. As exercise initiates the heart to pump more blood, the increased flow ensures that the needed oxygen is available to keep your brain healthy and strong. On the other hand, years of sedentary behavior and poor dietary habits can result in sluggish arterial flow to the brain, resulting in memory problems and other cognitive issues.

Exercise may also help reverse cellular deterioration associated with aging. Studies of small animals have shown that the increased blood flow stimulates the growth of *brain derived neurotrophic factor* (BDNF), a protein that supports brain cell growth and synaptic function, leading to a more efficient, sensitive, and adaptive brain.

Exercise to Reduce Alzheimer's Risk

Regular exercise may delay the onset of dementia and Alzheimer's disease according to research reported in the *Annals of Internal Medicine*. A 2006 study followed 1,740 people over the age of 65 and found that, over the course of six years, those who exercised at least three times a week were 32% less likely to be diagnosed with dementia during the study. The researchers concluded that the reduced risk may be because frequent exercisers have less brain tissue loss in the hippocampus, one of the earliest areas of the brain to be affected by Alzheimer's disease.

A 2009 study in the journal *The Physician and Sportsmedicine* notes that exercise can additionally promote the creation of new neurons, increasing brain volume and improving cognitive function. This provides aging brains with increased *plasticity*, the ability to create new neural connections. Not only does exercise increase the number of these connections, but it also improves their responsiveness and regulates important transmitters responsible for cell communication, helping your mind to become quick and agile.

Aerobic Conditioning, Strength, and Balance

Keeping the brain oxygenated and the mind strong requires a well-rounded fitness regimen that includes aerobic conditioning, strength, and balance training. Like the three primary colors that combine to create every color of the rainbow, these three areas of fitness work together to provide a full spectrum of body and brain health support.

Whether you create your own fitness training program or enlist the help of a personal trainer, aerobic, strength, and balance training should be a part of your overall exercise plan. It isn't necessary to fit each of these elements into every fitness session, but factoring them into your regular routine can help promote fitness for life.

Aerobic Conditioning to Oxygenate Your Brain

Also known as "cardio," aerobic exercise focuses on increasing the heart rate and providing oxygen-rich blood to the brain. Aerobic conditioning initiates deeper and faster breathing, training the heart, lungs, and blood vessels to become more efficient at delivering oxygen to all the cells in the body, including brain cells.

Thirty minutes of aerobic activity three times a week improves scores on memory tests and may reverse the effects of aging, according to James A. Blumenthal, PhD, of the Duke University Medical Center. Duke University research found that "aerobic exercise may not only lift depression in the middle-aged and elderly, but also improve memory, planning, organization, and the ability to juggle several mental tasks at the same time." As Dr. Blumenthal notes, regular aerobic exercise may be able to "offset some of the mental declines often associated with the aging process." You can receive aerobic benefits from all sorts of activities – raking leaves, washing dishes, playing with pets, or cleaning the house. Let's look at the activities that research has shown to be among the most effective aerobic exercise.

Walking

Walking is one of the simplest and most natural forms of aerobic exercise. It is low impact, doesn't require any special equipment, and you don't need a class to learn how to do it. In addition to cardiovascular benefits, walking helps to regulate metabolism and hormone production in a way that makes it easier to maintain healthy body weight. Walking can also be a meditative and relaxing experience, helping our body and minds to release the stress of the day.

AGELESS MIND FACT

A 2010 longitudinal study found that daily brisk walks can lower your risk for developing Alzheimer's disease or dementia by 40 percent.

In an era of "get fit quick" health devices and costly home exercise machines featured on late-night television, walking continues to be one of the easiest and cheapest ways to get an aerobic workout. How much walking should you do? In a study of more than 18,000 older women, Harvard researchers found that a total of 90 minutes a week of brisk walking, or about 15 minutes a day, was all that was needed to delay cognitive decline and reduce the risk for Alzheimer's disease.

Running

A study by the University of California Irvine's College of Medicine in 2002 showed that daily running or jogging may prevent brain cell deterioration. An ongoing research study compared lab rats that ran freely in mazes with those that did not. After three months, the running rats had developed twice as many new brain cells and demonstrated superior performance in maze-solving ability. The researchers concluded that physical activity helps regulate "neurogenesis, synaptic elasticity, and learning."

As the body ages, the high-impact nature of running might be just too much to take - especially those of us with bad knees and ankles. If, however, you are one of those people who just love to run, consider running on grass or dirt, or better yet, on the treadmill at the local gym. You can still quench your need for speed while helping to preserve those aging joints.

Cycling

Riding a bicycle is another great way to get, and stay, in shape. The smooth, circular movement of cycling not only provides an aerobic challenge, but can also strengthen troubled knee joints. Outdoor cycling is a great way to get some fresh air, but a stationary bike or elliptical machine offers a good alternative. Spinning classes have become increasingly popular and use different levels of resistance on stationary bikes to create an intense, concentrated workout. Many people find that the lively, social atmosphere found in spinning classes makes it easier to keep pedaling.

If you do choose to take your bicycle to the great outdoors, remember to wear a helmet and obey the rules of the road. Using a public park or bike path may provide a scenic way to enjoy your ride without the hassles and risks of city traffic.

Dancing

Dancing combines aerobic physical activity with emotional and sensory stimulation, social interaction, and motor coordination – what scientists call an "enriched environmental condition." Brain scans of experienced dancers show strengthened neural circuits in regions involved in motor control, as well as greater plasticity of their brains compared with the brains of novice dancers. Ruhr-University scientists in Germany found that people age 65 and older who had an average of nearly 17 years of amateur dancing under their belts had significantly better cognitive, motor, and perceptual abilities than a non-dancing control group.

Dancing is an effective all-around workout. The German author Johann Paul Friedrich Richter explains, "Other exercises develop single powers and muscles, but dancing embellishes, exercises, and equalizes all the muscles at once."

Swimming

Swimming not only offers a great cardiovascular workout, it engages almost every major muscle group in the body. Because it is a non-weight-bearing exercise, it is ideal for people who suffer from joint problems or other injuries. The buoyancy of water makes swimming one of the safest forms of low-impact exercise. Additionally, water offers twelve times more resistance than air, so moving through the pool is an efficient way to condition the heart and muscles. For those who do not swim, many pools offer organized water aerobics classes that do not require much, if any, swimming experience.

HEALTHY BRAIN TIP

Year-round swimming and water aerobics classes can be found at your local YMCA.

Swimming also provides a great means of relaxation and improves the spirit. In his 1883 book, <u>The Swimming Instructor,</u> William Wilson wrote "The experienced swimmer, when in the water, may be classed among the happiest of mortals in the happiest of moods, and in the most complete enjoyment of the happiest of exercises."

Aerobic Conditioning Tips

The type of aerobic conditioning you choose will depend on convenience and what fits best with your current lifestyle. Since the brain craves variety, try introducing new exercises to your daily routine.

Workout sessions don't have to last for hours; even a short walk around the block can have lasting benefits. Studies have found that multiple periods of brief exercise – such as three 10-minute sessions spread throughout the day – can be as effective in controlling weight and lowering the risk for heart disease as a single half-hour session.

The key is to start small and gradually build. As you increase your endurance, your heart and lungs become more efficient, providing better blood flow to the brain.

Start with a warm-up phase to raise your body temperature and loosen your joints. This will increase your pulse and prepare your heart for a more vigorous workout. After an aerobics session, take a few moments to cool down and gradually bring your body back to its resting state. Remember to stretch your muscles both before and after a workout to minimize soreness and increase flexibility.

Exercise Can Help Fight Depression

Anyone who has run a 10-K or done any kind of rigorous workout knows firsthand the feeling of endorphin-induced euphoria that often follows. We feel uplifted and clearheaded, and research suggests that it may have a lasting effect on relieving symptoms of depression.

1. 1. Researchers at Duke University compared the antidepressant effects of aerobic exercise training to the antidepressant sertraline (Zoloft®), as well as a placebo pill. After four months, they found that exercise was just as good or better than the Zoloft® in treating depression. Those who exercised at a moderate level – about 40 minutes three to five days each week – experienced the greatest antidepressant effect.

2. Exercise not only releases endorphins, the body's own natural antidepressant; it also releases the brain messenger serotonin, which elevates mood. Many of today's antidepressants like Zoloft® or Prozac® work with the brain's chemistry by increasing the amount of serotonin, a chemical that is decreased in depression. So not only will exercise help keep you physically healthy - the chemical reaction in the brain can also boost your mood.

Strength and Resistance Training

Most of us have seen body builders who lift huge barbells to enlarge their muscles and sculpt their bodies. They're usually trying to build larger biceps, washboard abs, and stronger hamstrings. While most people think of weight lifting as an activity reserved for young muscle-bound athletes, research shows that older people, even those in their nineties, can benefit from pumping iron, too. Neuroscientists are now finding that strength and resistance training also support brain fitness.

In studies of middle-aged women at the University of British Columbia, Dr. Terese Liu-Ambrose found that those who engaged in weight lifting had better cognitive abilities than those who only did stretching and toning activities. Strength training seems to improve specific brain functions involving complex reasoning and attention skills that are controlled in the frontal lobe. Pumping iron builds brain muscle by increasing the heart's efficiency in supplying blood to the brain.

Resistance and strength training not only protects brain health and builds muscle mass, but it also helps makes bones denser and lowers the risk for osteoporosis, which can make bones more brittle with age. In a study reported in the *New England Journal of Medicine*, researchers from Tufts University engaged nursing home residents in a ten-week program of supervised weight training. The researchers concluded that "a high-intensity, progressive regimen of resistance training improves muscle strength and size in elderly people." Other studies confirm that weight training with either free weights or machines helps to restore diminished bone density, reduces arthritis pain, and dramatically increases functional strength. Consider the following strength-training exercises for building up your body and brain.

Working With Weights

Training with free weights can help isolate and strengthen specific muscle groups. Free weights come in a variety of shapes and sizes, providing everything from 1-pound wrist weights to the cartoonishly large barbells as seen in competitions. When working with weights, it is often a good idea to consult with a trainer or someone with experience who can help you learn

> **HEALTHY BRAIN TIP**
>
> When starting out at home, large cans of corn or beans make great beginner weights.

correct form so that your workout is injury-free and supports good balance and coordination.

If you work out in a gym, you can achieve similar benefits with weight-lifting machines. These machines help guide the weight-lifting motions and reinforce correct posture. Working with a trainer can also help by showing you how to increase the effectiveness of a machine workout and reduce the risk of injury. Whether you choose free weights or a gym machine, remember to start out small, then as your strength increases, build up your repetitions and slowly add weight to meet your fitness goals.

Resistance and Isometric Exercises

Another way to enjoy the benefits of weight training is through resistance bands. These safe and convenient bands, available almost everywhere lately, come in varying degrees of resistance and can be used to work out upper and lower body muscle groups. If you don't have an assortment of bands available, you can wrap or double-up your available band to make it tighter and increase its resistance as you get stronger. Since elastic bands are light in weight, they are easy to pack and great for keeping up your exercise program when you travel.

Without a band, you can do isometric exercises which involve muscular contractions with no movement. An example of a simple isometric exercise that will strengthen your upper body is to sit up straight and push your hands together in front of your chest. Breathe slowly and deeply and hold for five seconds, then rest between reps. Since you are using the resistance of your own body, these and similar exercises can be done anywhere and with no equipment. In fact, you can try it right now!

Balance and Stability for Healthy Aging

As we get older, balance and stability become an increasingly important part of healthy aging. Since loss of balance and stability is directly related to an increased risk of injury from falls, it is in our best interest to include this type of fitness in our daily regimen.

Older research volunteers who incorporate balance training in their exercise programs also show significant improvements in memory and other cognitive abilities. Exercises that improve balance stimulate brain neural circuits to send messages from the brain to the body, making it better able to right itself if it becomes unsteady. These neural networks inform us how to act and how much tension is needed in each muscle group in order to remain upright. The brain health benefits of balance and stability exercises could result, in part, from this focused form of cognitive training.

Physical balance and stability have a profound affect on our safety, grace, and composure throughout life. We can prevent age-related injury associated with loss of balance and poise with some simple practices.

Single-Leg Standing

Balance and stability training doesn't have to require special equipment. Standing on one leg (like a flamingo) while looking in the mirror is a simple and effective training exercise. Start out by counting to 10, keeping on eye on the mirror for help. You may want to stand near something stable, like a table or a wall to steady yourself if necessary. Once you are able to remain balanced for 30 seconds on each leg, try doing it with your eyes closed. You may be surprised at how difficult this is at first, but keep practicing and build up your physical confidence.

AGELESS MIND FACT

The current world record for standing on one leg with eyes closed - while holding an umbrella - is 2 minutes.

Tai Chi

Originally developed as a powerful martial art, this popular Eastern practice uses slow and deliberate movements that offer several brain health benefits. The meditative component reduces stress while the smooth movements improve cardiovascular conditioning, balance, and stability. Steven L. Wolf, PhD, and his colleagues at the Emory University School of Medicine found that older adults who participated in a fifteen-week tai chi program reported significant improvements in balance, and they reduced their risk of falling by almost 50%.

There are a number of different styles of tai chi - all are characterized by fluid, slow, graceful movements. For the older participants, this "meditation in motion" has surprising benefits. According to Gloria Yeh, MD, from Harvard Medical School, "Tai chi strengthens both the lower and upper extremities and also the core muscles of the back and abdomen." If you are just starting out, it is best to learn tai chi from an accomplished teacher, but once you learn good form, you can practice it on your own.

Pilates

This exercise system was developed by Joseph Pilates as a way for people to increase strength, flexibility, and coordination. It incorporates controlled movements that strengthen the body's core muscles, including the stomach, lower back, buttocks, and inner thighs. These muscle groups provide the body's structural support that maintains balance and stability. A recent study found that middle-aged people who attended a 12-week Pilates class for an hour twice weekly showed significant improvement in objective measures of balance and posture.

Although a full Pilates program requires the assistance of an instructor and special Pilates equipment, simpler exercises based on the same principles can be done on your own.

More Dancing!

Dancing not only offers aerobic conditioning benefits; it also helps people stay balanced. Investigators at Aristotle University in Greece assessed the effect of a ten-week traditional Greek dance program on objective measures of balance in healthy older adults. They found that the dance group showed significant

> **HEALTHY BRAIN TIP**
> Check the local community center or ballroom for social dancing lessons and events.

improvements in balance when standing and moving compared to a control group. Other studies have found that older adults who are regular social dancers have better balance and stability when standing or walking compared to non-dancers. Whether you like to cha-cha, fox trot, or polka, dancing can be a way to have fun while improving your balance and stability.

Conclusions

Whether you enjoy tai chi, Pilates, or prefer to dance the night away, some form of daily movement practice is essential as we get older. Whatever your stage in life or your current state of fitness, you can become stronger, better balanced, and more poised starting today.

Computer Games for Balance and Fitness

For many aging adults, heading to the bowling alley or playing a round of golf is not a physical or logistical option. For those who are unable to participate in these activities, computer games may provide an alternative.

1. The popularity of such interactive gaming platforms as the Nintendo Wii® and the XBox Kinect® has marked a new era in fitness options. Players can now become physically engaged in digital versions of bowling, tennis, golf, and even skiing without leaving the house. The exercise benefits are the result of using the body to control the action, compared to more sedentary video games where only a hand-held controller is required.

2. Interactive computer games also flex your mental muscles. As the brain becomes challenged by the action on the screen, it sends signals to the entire body, strengthening neural connections that govern the body's vital systems. When the body reacts, for example, to the tennis ball in the game, it reinforces that connection and increases the brain's speed and agility.

Tips For Starting an Exercise Program

Find Activities You Enjoy

One of the secrets of fitness is to find activities that you want to do, which increases your motivation for doing them. If you are out of shape, you may think that the only activity you enjoy is resting on the couch. Nevertheless, you will discover that if you get up and exercise, you will be glad you did. Imagine the feeling of relaxation and exhilaration that comes from a good workout, and let that feeling launch you off of the couch and into activity. Some people like going to the gym while others prefer dancing, biking, or yoga. Try different fitness activities and find the ones that are most fun to you.

Warm Up and Cool Down

When you engage in aerobic exercise or strength training, your cells send messages to the brain that say, "Please expand the blood supply." The results are greater cardiovascular capacity and stronger muscles. This process, however, takes time for the body to become ready for exertion. The best strategy is to gently warm up in preparation for exercise and then to give yourself enough time to cool down after you finish. An appropriate warm-up increases the flow of fluid in your joints and blood to your muscles in a way that helps lower the risk of injury. Ending with a "cool down" period allows your body to recover from the demands you've placed upon it while exercising.

Quit While You're Ahead

This is an important piece of common sense that is often forgotten. If you stop exercising while still enjoying it, then you will create a positive *recency effect* - the term psychologists use to describe the tendency to remember the last thing in a series. The positive feeling at the end of your exercise period makes it much easier to look forward to your next session. Let go of the outdated and destructive notion of "no pain, no gain." Instead, try a more measured approach and focus on making the most of every workout.

Form Is Almost Everything

The way you do an exercise is profoundly important. If the body is contorted when doing a stretch or lifting a weight, you will do more harm than good. Proper form is essential for a safe and effective fitness program. It is often the quality of training that influences your progress more than the quantity. As with all exercises, understanding the proper mechanics of training allows you to get the most benefit from your time.

Make Exercise a Part of Daily Life

While attending a dance class or fitness program can be a great way to focus our attention on exercise, experts agree that it is best to take a long-term approach. Make an effort to embrace the fitness opportunities in everyday life. For example, whenever you can, take the stairs instead of the elevator.

Stretch while waiting in line at the bank. Park a little farther away from the store and enjoy the walk. Finding small ways to stay physically healthy throughout the day will help us view exercise less a short-term activity and more as a lifestyle.

Physical Fitness and Your Ageless Mind

Scientific studies have demonstrated that a lower risk for Alzheimer's disease is associated with almost any form of daily physical activity, whether it's gardening, housework, swimming, or tennis. In a 2008 study in the *Journal of the American Geriatrics Society*, researchers asked more than 2,700 women in their eighties to wear a wrist monitor that measured all of their daily movement, from walking to shopping to gardening. The women who were the most active showed better mental function and were the least likely to show signs of cognitive impairment.

An ideal fitness program incorporates complementary areas of fitness including cardiovascular conditioning, strength and flexibility training, and the cultivation of balance and poise. As we age, these three dimensions of fitness all serve to support the vigor of the body and the stength of your ageless mind.

Your Ageless Lifestyle

Lifestyle is one of the major factors determining brain health. The good news is that while some areas of your health (such as genetics) cannot be changed, your ability to establish brain-benefiting lifestyle strategies is under your complete control. Part of an ageless lifestyle means engaging with others socially, practicing healthy stress management, and focusing on lifelong learning. In the chapters that follow, we will explore how these, and other areas, help to support your ageless mind.

CHAPTER **SIX**

6

Stress

> *If you ask what is the single most important key to longevity, I would say it is avoiding worry, stress, and tension. And if you didn't ask me, I'd still have to say it.*

George Burns

This is your brain on stress

Since our earliest days, the human brain has been programmed to respond to stress in a way that would ensure the survival of the species. Our ancestors relied upon stress to stimulate a fight-or-flight reaction, signaling their brains to release a flurry of stress hormones that enabled them to quickly respond to the life-threatening dangers around them.

But what about today when the internet goes down or you can't find your credit card? Nowadays, when our stress is caused by such daily occurrences, this hard-wired stress response can build up and become chronic, resulting in those same hormones causing wear and tear on our neurons, worsening our memory, and possibly contributing to Alzheimer's disease.

AGELESS MIND FACT

When it comes to creating a stress response, the brain is unable to distinguish between real and perceived (psychological) threats.

Researchers at the University of Wisconsin are finding that the stress stimulated by modern threats causes a shift in the natural balance of attention in the brain, disrupting the ability to solve complex problems and think with less clarity. When the brain shifts into a stress-alert mode, it must process a large amount of data by quickly scanning the environment in an attempt to detect danger. This series of events creates a form of information overload that actually impairs attention and problem solving. Studies of electrical activity in the brain during an acute stress attack show a shift away from the brain's frontal executive centers in the *amygdala*, an area beneath the temples that controls a range of emotional reactions. When confronted with stress, the emotional amygdala takes over, and we tend to react quickly and instinctively, with less thought, and we often have trouble making reasonable decisions.

Cortisol is one of the hormones that the body creates while under stress, helping us adapt to severe threats. When released, cortisol shifts blood flow to the brain to help focus attention. Blood is also moved from the stomach to the muscles as the brain senses impending danger. In this process, appetite declines as muscles receive the increased energy and strength needed to handle the perceived threat.

Studies show that after several days of cortisol injections, human volunteers experienced impaired verbal memory ability, as well as considerable difficulty remembering information they had just read. The good news is that these impairments are temporary. Memory ability returns once cortisol levels revert to normal. It is also interesting to note that other studies indicate that when the brain is stressed, some forms of emotional memory may actually improve, which is consistent with the data showing that the amygdala's emotional center may become more active in stressful situations.

Symptoms of Stress

We all react differently to triggers of stress and anxiety, and this creates a range of symptoms, both physical and psychological. The chart belows shows how stress can manifest itself in the body and mind. Even in cases where the cause of stress is merely perceived, the resulting symptoms are very real.

Physical Symptoms	Mental Symptoms
Aches and Pains	Anger
Change in Appetite	Anxiety
Fatigue	Depression
Cold Hands and Feet	Fear
Headache	Frustration
Insomnia	Impatience
Nail-Biting	Feeling Under Pressure
Rapid Heart Rate	Poor Concentration
Sweating	Irritability
Trembling	Poor Sense of Humor
Trouble Swallowing	Confusion
Upset Stomach	Memory Loss

Anger

Anger is a common symptom of stress, and evidence shows it can spike your heart rate and blood pressure, potentially raising the risk of heart problems. While early research showed that anger in general is harmful for your heart, new studies suggest that how you express your anger matters more. For example, a 2009 study published in the *British Journal of Health Psychology* demonstrated that suppressing anger has both immediate and delayed cardiovascular consequences. In addition, a 2010 study in the *American Heart Journal* found that men and women who blamed others for their anger increased their heart disease risk as much as 31%. Men in the study who discussed their anger to resolve a situation, on the other hand, lowered their chances of developing heart disease.

The studies on anger illustrate an important truth: Since our lives will likely always contain some chaos, our focus needs to be on responding well to stressful situations. That pays dividends beyond keeping your heart healthy and young – it can also help you get more satisfaction out of your now-longer life. To deal with anger in a healthy way, choose your battles. Don't suppress your anger and stew about it. Find a trusted confidant you can vent to, but use the conversation to help you move past anger, not dwell on it.

Stress and Risk for Alzheimer's

We know that stress can create havoc in our lives and can contribute to a variety of physical illnesses ranging from ulcers to heart disease. It also poses a threat to brain health and increases an individual's risk for Alzheimer's disease. Dr. Lena Johansson and colleagues at the University of Gothenburg in Sweden assessed levels of psychological stress in more than 1,100 women between the ages of 38 and 60. Her research group defined stress as a symptom of nervousness, irritation, tension, fear, or sleep problems. After following these women for 35 years, the scientists discovered that those who experienced frequent stress in mid life had a 65% greater risk for Alzheimer's disease compared to those who did not experience frequent stress.

The studies of human volunteers are consistent with previous work done with stressed-out animals. Dr. Robert Sapolsky of Stanford University has shown that chronic stress in laboratory mice leads to atrophy, or shrinkage, of the *hippocampus*, a brain area that controls memory processing, and the animals with a smaller hippocampus have trouble finding their way through mazes. Sapolsky's group agrees with other neuroscientists that stress hormones may be damaging the brain and aggravating a chronic inflammatory response.

Meditation can help the brain fight stress

Neuroscientists now have evidence that meditating helps reduce stress and improves mental focus. In one study, Dr. Britta Hölzel and associates at Harvard Medical School put volunteers on a meditation program. The study subjects meditated 30 minutes a day, using a form of meditation involving focused attention on sensations that include deep breathing and learning to bring the mind back to breathing if it wandered off. MRI scans taken at the beginning and after eight weeks of meditating showed that the test subjects had increased the volume of grey matter in the hippocampus, while the non-meditating control group showed no change.

AGELESS MIND FACT

A Harvard research study estimates that 60-90% of all doctor's visits are the result of stress-related problems.

Meditation also fires up the frontal areas of the brain that are associated with attention and relaxation. In people with memory loss, meditation improves performance on challenging memory tests. After just three months of meditation training, volunteers became better able to release thoughts that popped into their minds, improving their ability to focus attention. Meditation not only strengthens the brain's memory and attention centers; it also appears to fortify the neural circuits that control our emotions. Brief meditation breaks throughout the day can result in a sense of calm that often improves a person's feeling of well-being.

Laughter – the Best Medicine

Humor is infectious. The sound of roaring laughter is far more contagious than any cough, sniffle, or sneeze. When laughter is shared, it binds people together and increases happiness and intimacy. Laughter also triggers healthy physical changes in the body. Good humor strengthens the immune system, boosts energy, diminishes pain, and prevents the damaging effects of stress. Best of all, this priceless medicine is fun, free, and easy to use.

Researchers at the Loma Linda University School of Medicine's Department of Clinical Immunology conducted numerous studies proving that laughter helps lower stress hormones, increases the number of helpful anti-body cells, and enhances the efficiency of T-cells. In other words, laughter helps stimulate the immune system and counters the immunosuppressive effect of stress. Laughter also benefits the heart, improves oxygen flow to the brain, and works the muscles in the head, neck, chest and pelvis - similar to stress reduction exercises used in yoga. This helps keep muscles loose and limber and enables them to rest more easily.

Laughter may protect against heart disease, as well. In a study of 300 volunteers, scientists found that the people without heart disease were 60% more likely to see the humor in everyday life. Other studies have linked watching a daily half-hour sitcom with lower blood pressure and improved heartbeat regularity, both of which lower the risk of heart attacks.

HEALTHY BRAIN TIP

Feeling under the weather? A comedy movie marathon and plenty of chicken soup will have you healthy in no time.

Simply remembering a good laugh decreases the stress chemicals cortisol and epinephrine by 39% and 70%, respectively, say researchers at Loma Linda University. Laughter is also great for the heart. When participants in a University of Maryland study watched stressful film clips, they experienced ***vasoconstriction*** - a narrowing of the blood vessels - while the blood vessels of those watching funny films expanded by 22%.

Top 10 Benefits of Laughter

Whether you are enjoying the latest comedy at the theater or spending a light-hearted evening with friends, laughter gives us many important physical and cognitive benefits. Here are 10 of the ways that laughter strengthens your body and mind:

- Lowers blood pressure.

- Increases vascular blood flow and oxygenation of blood.

- Gives a workout to the diaphragm and abdominal, respiratory, facial, leg, and back muscles.

- Defends against respiratory infections – even reducing the frequency of colds – by increasing immuno-globulin in saliva.

- Increases memory and learning; in a study at Johns Hopkins Medical School, humor during instruction led to improved test scores.

- Reduces the level of stress hormones such as cortisol, epinephrine, and adrenaline.

- Increases the level of endorphins, feel-good hormones.

- Increases neurotransmitter connections in the brain.

- Supports the immune system by increasing the number of anti-body producing cells and enhancing the efficiency of T-cells.

- Laughter improves mood and makes you feel great!

Humor and the Brain

Humor works quickly. Less than a half-second after exposure to something funny, an electrical wave moves through the higher brain functions of the cerebral cortex. The left hemisphere analyzes the words and structure of the joke; the right hemisphere "gets" the joke; the visual sensory area of the occipital lobe creates images; the limbic (emotional) system makes you happier; and the motor sections make you smile or laugh.

"Laughter is all about relationships," says Robert Provine, professor at the University of Maryland. In fact, you may be "tuned" for laughter from family and culture, creating a coping mechanism for relieving stress.

What is happening in your brain when you just have to laugh? The neural network, in both the frontal and temporal regions, regulates the perception of humor. We have all developed different networks and find different things funny. When something strikes you as hilarious, your brain networks induce facial reactions. It starts with smiles, and if the humor is really funny, the brainstem gets the laughter going.

Laughter also eases muscle tension and encourages the lungs to take deeper breaths. A 2001 study reported in the *Journal of the American Medical Association* showed that symptoms improved in allergy patients who viewed comedic movies, but not in those in the control group, who watched weather reports. Laughter boosts immunity and also "increases our heart rate, helps us breathe more deeply, and stretches many different muscles in our face and upper body," according to research by Richard Wiseman, PhD. "In fact," he adds, "it is like a mini workout."

Humor also improves cognitive function by keeping the mind active and encouraging creative thinking – a vital defense against age. According to humor guru William Fry, MD, of Stanford University, "Humor and creativity work in similar ways by creating relationships between two disconnected items, engaging the whole brain."

Laughter and Pain Management

Everyone likes a good laugh. Humor allows us to release tension and let go of fearful or angry feelings, even if just for a little while. Norman Cousins was a champion of using humor to battle his painful and crippling arthritic disease, and systematic research has supported such health-promoting effects of humor.

In his classic book, <u>Anatomy of an Illness as Perceived by the Patient</u>, Norman Cousins shares the story of his recovery from a form of severe degenerative arthritis. His most successful therapy was laughter. He watched funny movies and surrounded himself with humor. "I made the joyous discovery that 10 minutes of genuine belly laughter has an anesthetic effect," he wrote.

Many studies have proven Cousins right, showing that laughter has a pain-relieving effect (most likely because it releases endorphins in the bloodstream), especially for chronic pain from arthritis or neurological diseases.

Smile Power

Surround yourself with laughter. Smile and laugh for no reason. The great psychological pioneer William James explained, "We don't laugh because we are happy. We are happy because we laugh." James' assertion is supported by current research. Paul Ekman, PhD, and his associates have demonstrated that smiling improves mood and positively influences the mood of others.

Smiling encourages a more kind and generous responses to others. It is a contagious expression, like yawning and laughing, and helps you connect better, which in turn, stimulates the brain. A smile helps you look younger and feel healthier as it lowers your blood pressure and boosts the activity of the immune system.

> **HEALTHY BRAIN TIP**
> Smiling can work like magic. The next time you're feeling down, try smiling and see what a difference it makes.

Smiling can also be good for the brain. Smiling helps your mood and attitude become more positive, and it reduces stress. Smiling helps the brain release more endorphins and ***enkephalins*** (the body's natural painkillers), as well as ***serotonin*** (which regulates mood, appetite, sleep, and some cognitive functions).

Stress and Your Ageless Mind

Americans report a significantly lower incidence of worry and stress as they get older, particularly as they move into and beyond their mid-50s. This finding runs counter to the hypothesis that those who are older would be more apt to worry about health, money, or other issues.

After 50, daily stress and worry take a dive and daily happiness increases, according to an analysis of more than 340,000 adults questioned about the emotions they experienced "yesterday."

The research, published in the journal *Proceedings of the National Academy of Sciences*, shows that young adults experience more negative emotions more frequently than those who are older. Negative emotions, such as stress and anger, are similar in that they consistently decline with age, but worry holds steady until around 50, when it sharply drops, the study shows.

One belief is that older adults are simply more experienced at handling stress. It seems inevitable that over the course of a long life, there will be certain emotional highs and lows. Older adults seem to have a more "been there, done that" perspective. They can view stressors within a context of other experiences they have encountered over time.

Whether at age 30 or 90, it is likely that stress is a part of your life. Staying physically and mentally fit over the long term means finding constructive ways of dealing with the stress as it comes. It is through these coping strategies that you can begin to nurture your happy and healthy ageless mind.

CHAPTER SEVEN

Social Network

*" Those who love deeply
never grow old; they may die of
old age, but they
die young. "*

Benjamin Franklin

CULTIVATE HEALTHY RELATIONSHIPS

Many studies demonstrate the importance of vibrant social interaction to support healthy aging. *The American Journal of Public Health* reported on a study of more than two thousand older women conducted over four years. Participants were interviewed to determine the extent and liveliness of their social lives. The women were asked questions such as, "How many people can you rely on for help?" and "How many people can you confide in?" Researchers also monitored the number of the participants' social visits, phone calls, emails, and other forms of social communication. The results? Women with more expansive social networks were at significantly less risk of cognitive decline. And those who engaged in meaningful daily interaction with family and friends were almost 50% less likely to develop dementia.

Valerie C. Crooks, director of the study, explains, "Whenever we have even the most basic exchange, we have to think about how to respond, and that stimulates the brain. There are people who are outliers, who have two very close relationships and are fine cognitively. But people who have three or more relationships do better." Crooks summarizes the findings this way: "If you are socially engaged, you are at a lower risk of dementia."

Researchers from the Rush University Alzheimer's Disease Center in Chicago studied a group of eight hundred adults over 80. At the beginning of the four-year study, the subjects were all free from symptoms of cognitive decline. The participants completed an assessment designed to measure their relative degree of social integration. Those who reported that they were lonely were more than twice as likely to develop symptoms of dementia during the course of the study than those with richer social lives.

Health Benefits of a Social Network

A strong, healthy network of relationships protects against more than dementia. Studies have also demonstrated that strong social networks and support groups can help people recover from a wide range of ailments. Stanford University's David Spiegel, MD, and his colleagues published a landmark paper in the medical journal *The Lancet* reporting that women with breast cancer who participated in support groups experienced less pain and lived twice as long as those who didn't participate in such groups. Other studies have shown that people with more friends tend to live longer after surviving a heart attack than those without a supportive social network. Even for germaphobes who worry about the exposure of social interaction, there's considerable evidence that the immune-strengthening benefits of friendships outweigh the risks. People with more friends have fewer colds and recover faster when they do catch one.

A Case of Loneliness

Loneliness isn't just an issue for older people; it has become a pandemic in our society. In 2006, the American Sociological Review published a study showing that social isolation affects people of all ages and that it is more prevalent now than ever before. Almost 25% of the subjects in this comprehensive research project reported that they had no one in whom to confide, a percentage that had more than doubled in the previous two decades.

John T. Cacioppo, PhD, a psychologist at the University of Chicago, has researched the relationship between social psychology and neuroscience for more than thirty years. In 2008, with co-author William Patrick, Cacioppo published the ground-breaking book, Loneliness: Human Nature and the Need for Social Connection. Cacioppo and Patrick made a powerful case that a healthy social network is a major determinant of overall mental health and physical well-being. Together they have pioneered the emerging discipline of social neuroscience. They argue that our brains are hard-wired to thrive through social interaction. As Cacioppo and Patrick comment, "Our sociality is central to who we are."

Social Ties and the Brain

It goes without saying that keeping up positive relationships with family and friends is emotionally and socially rewarding. In addition to supporting overall health, it is also good for the brain. The MacArthur study on aging and other research suggest that social support can improve mental performance.

A Canadian study published in 2003 sought to tease out the effect of social engagement on cognitive function in a group of adults over 65. Over the course of the study, researchers found that social ties were a strong predictor of cognitive functioning. Results showed that the probability of maintaining strong cognitive function was highest among those who socialized often and had good social ties, and the probability of losing cognitive function was highest among participants who were not socially engaged. The researchers concluded that weak social ties and activity were risk factors for cognitive decline.

Social Ties and Memory

There are several reasons why maintaining an active social life may help prevent memory loss. Interpersonal engagement may increase the likelihood of ongoing involvement in intellectually stimulating activities. Social connectedness also helps cushion the blow from stressful life events and, therefore, reduces the negative effect that stress can exert on the brain.

You might wonder if all social ties are good. In other words, should you mend fences with a disagreeable in-law or an annoying neighbor just because it might be good for you? Probably not, unless you think that relationship is worth repairing. The best relationships are the ones you feel drawn to; they make you feel engaged, challenged, and supported.

"Social behavior is a brain function just like memory or language," says Dr. John Ratey in User's Guide to the Brain. "The social brain helps individuals and the clan of humans survive."

Getting "Out There"

Social functions energize the whole brain. You remember faces, names, talk about politics, move your body, have feelings, think about what you hear, watch what you eat – all at the same time. "Our highest human virtue is our connection with other humans, and social activity is basic to our health and happiness," says Dr. Ratey.

When you engage in social functions, your brain works better. Married men live an average of ten years longer than non-married men, according to the Population Research Association of America. Those over the age of seventy who had strong friendships were 22% more likely to live more than ten years longer than those who didn't, according to the Australian Longitudinal Study of Aging.

A rich social network may decrease the risk of developing dementia, according to Swedish research, because it increases social interaction and intellectual stimulation. The National Institute of Mental Health says that participating in religious, social, or other activities can help depression.

No matter whether you're shy, have lost friends due to relocation or deaths, or are uncomfortable with social interactions and small talk, you can still maximize your social brain.

> **AGELESS MIND FACT**
>
> According to a survey in *Psychology Today,* 64% of the responders said that they felt shy every day; 24% said it affected their plans.

Invest in Your Social Wealth

Most people understand the importance of saving money and allowing their savings to grow interest and pay dividends over time. What many people don't realize is the importance of investing in their social capital as well. John T. Cacioppo has coined the term "social wealth" to refer to the abundance of positive, healthy relationships that serve to nurture us in a variety of practical ways. A rich social life will help prevent cognitive decline as it strengthens the immune system. Here are some simple practices and ideas for cultivating a social network.

- **Feel connected.** Feeling connected by social ties or networks has a direct positive effect on mortality and health. The benefits of social networks can come from families, groups of friends, groups sponsored by community organizations, or churches. Even internet-based networks are now being used by people of all ages to provide social and informational interaction and support.

- **Take classes.** Expand your social network by learning with others. When you learn chess, languages, tai chi, yoga, flower arranging, cooking, or painting along with others you multiply the benefits.

- **Cherish friendships.** True friendships are rare and precious. When you identify current or potential true friends, do your best to cultivate and cherish the relationship. The benefits of close friendships multiply as the years go by. As Thomas Jefferson wrote, "I find friendship to be like wine, raw when new, ripened with age…the true restorative cordial… The happiest moments my heart knows are those in which it is pouring forth its affections to a few esteemed characters."

- **Take the social initiative.** Rather than waiting for invitations, take the initiative: Invite potential friends for dinner or to a movie, concert, or lecture.

- **Dine with others.** As the Italians say, A tavola non si invecchia – "at the table, you don't grow old." Sharing a meal with others daily is one of the practices common to the world's longest-living people, according Dan Buettner, author of, <u>The Blue Zones: Lessons in Living Longer from the People Who've Lived the Longest</u>.

- **Volunteer.** Caring for others is one of the surest ways to feel better about yourself. Helping out at a soup kitchen, animal shelter, hospice, or school provides a sense of meaning and purpose that keeps you sharp and more fulfilled.

- **Mentor younger people.** Older people who provide intergenerational guidance experience profound benefits. A study by Elizabeth Larkin and her colleagues, published in the *Journal of Gerontological Social Work*, reports that "mentoring experiences allow opportunities for older adults to renew positive emotions and reinforce meaning in their lives."

- **Surround yourself with positive people.** Socializing isn't automatically beneficial. It has to be fundamentally positive to yield brain benefits. Negative relationships characterized by whining, complaining, judging, and abusive language can, according to some studies, be detrimental to our cognitive and emotional lives. You may find, however, that if you embrace an optimistic, upbeat attitude, it becomes easier to meet other optimistic, upbeat people.

- **Continuously improve your listening skills.** Listening is like driving – most people think they are better than average, but, of course, that can't be true. The best listeners adopt an attitude of humility, empathy, and continuous improvement. As playwright Wilson Mizner observed, "A good listener is not only popular everywhere, but after a while he gets to know something."

According to researchers, the more people participate in close social relationships, the better their overall physical and mental health, and the higher their level of function. The definition of "social relationship" is broad and can include everything from daily phone chats with family to regular visits with close friends to attending church every Sunday. The MacArthur Foundation Study on Aging revealed that the two strongest predictors of well-being among older people are: frequency of visits with friends and frequency of attendance at organization meetings. The more meaningful the contribution in a particular activity, the greater the health benefit. It doesn't always have to be people who believe what you believe. Studies show that the more diverse our innermost circle of social support, the better off we are.

> **HEALTHY BRAIN TIP**
>
> Life is too short to not share it with those around us. Reach out to someone and make a connection today.

Prayer and Meditation

Maintaining a regular prayer life or meditative practice creates many health benefits, mostly by calming the stress response. Physicians Larry Dossey, author of Healing Words, Dale Mathews, author of The Faith Factor, and others have written books outlining the scientific evidence for the medical benefits of prayer and other meditative states. Some of these benefits include reduced feelings of stress, lower cholesterol levels, improved sleep, reduced anxiety and depression, fewer headaches, more relaxed muscles, and a longer life-span. People who pray or read the Bible every day are 40% less likely to suffer from hypertension than others. A Duke University study of 577 men and women hospitalized for physical illness showed that the more patients used positive spiritual coping strategies (seeking spiritual support from friends and religious leaders, having faith in God, praying), the lower their level of depressive symptoms and the higher their quality of life. In a follow-up survey of 269 family physicians, 99% believed prayer, meditation, and other spiritual and religious practices can be helpful in medical treatment; more than half said they currently incorporate relaxation or meditative techniques into the treatment of patients.

Meditation Under the Microscope

Using brain SPECT imaging, Andrew Newberg and his colleagues at the University of Pennsylvania investigated the neurobiology of meditation, in part because it is a spiritual state easily duplicated in the laboratory. They scanned nine Buddhist monks both before and during prolonged meditation. The scan revealed distinctive changes in brain activity as the mind went into a meditative state. Specifically, activity decreased in the parts of the brain involved in generating a sense of three-dimensional orientation in space. Losing one's sense of physical space could account for the spiritual feeling of transcendence, being beyond space and time. They also found increased activity in the prefrontal cortex, which is associated with attention span and thoughtfulness. Meditation allowed the subjects to find their "calming centers," diminishing anxiety and fostering relaxation.

> **AGELESS MIND FACT**
>
> Meditation is the most common alternative therapy in the U.S. with an estimated 10 million participants, according to a 2009 survey.

Throughout history, various forms of religion and spirituality have been a way for people to embrace a more positive outlook and find deeper meaning in life. Although organized religion is a major influence in many people's lives throughout the world, spirituality is a broad concept and isn't necessarily connected to a specific belief system or form of worship. Some people satisfy their spiritual needs through meditation, music, or art, while others seek harmony with nature or the universe. Whatever form your spiritual expression takes, it can not only provide a feeling of security and manage stress, but can also extend your life expectancy.

Religion and Longevity

Several scientific studies have found that regular church attendance is associated with longer life. One recent study showed that visiting a house of worship just once each week extends average life expectancy by seven years. The scientists found that the church-going/longevity connection held up even when they factored out the influences of social support and healthy lifestyles associated with organized religion.

Some people believe that faith in a higher power keeps them healthy and heals their illnesses. Dr. Kenneth Pargament and his associates at Bowling Green State University in Ohio studied nearly six hundred medical patients and found that those who believed in God had a 30% lower mortality rate as compared with those who felt abandoned by God. Dr. Harold Koenig and his colleagues at Duke University interviewed over eight hundred medical patients and found that those embracing religious beliefs or some type of spirituality had better social support, less depression, and higher cognitive function.

Mainstream medicine is recognizing the importance of the interaction between spirituality and health. Neuroscientists have been able to pinpoint specific areas of the brain that are activated when people pray. The meditative state typical of intense prayer has been found to lower blood pressure and heart rate, which reduces the body's stress response. Nearly two out of every three U.S. medical schools now offer courses on spirituality. Some medical students actually follow the hospital chaplains on their rounds to learn firsthand how the clergy help people who are suffering from physical illness.

Heart surgery patients who said they received strength and comfort from their religion were three times more likely to survive than those who did not, report researchers at the Dartmouth-Hitchcock Medical Center in Lebanon, New Hampshire. A study of 113 women at the University of North Carolina in Greensboro found a strong link between lower blood pressure and strong religious beliefs – even after factoring in such things as weight, diet, and other lifestyle issues. A study of nearly 92,000 men and women by researchers at Johns Hopkins University in Baltimore found that weekly church-goers died 50% less often from heart disease, emphysema, and suicide, and 74% less often from cirrhosis of the liver, than people who did not attend church.

Medical patients across a large spectrum have cited religion or spirituality as a key component in their recoveries. While western medicine has been slow to acknowledge the clinical benefits, studies continue to come in supporting the faith-health connection.

Adopt a Pet

Those of us who own pets know they make us happy. But a growing body of scientific research is showing that our pets can also make us healthy, or at least healthier.

After conducting health evaluations of almost 6,000 people, 784 of whom were pet owners, Dr. Warwick Anderson discovered that the pet owners had significantly lower cholesterol counts and blood pressure readings. They also reported experiencing less stress. According to James Serpell, author of In the Company of Animals, A Study of Human-Animal Relationships, the benefits of caring for a pet are stronger than "the known effects of other positive lifestyle factors such as regular exercise or low-fat diets." He adds, "Pet owners also reported improved psychological well-being and self-esteem scores compared with a group of non-owners."

Pets and Health

While pet owners always suspected that owning a pet was good for you, it wasn't until the late 1970s that researchers began to uncover the science behind the bond. One of the earliest studies, published in 1980, found that heart attack patients who owned pets lived longer than those who didn't. Another early study found that petting one's own dog could reduce blood pressure.

> **HEALTHY BRAIN TIP**
>
> Are you considering getting a cat or dog? Try the local animal shelter first. When you adopt a pet, everyone wins.

"More recently," says Rebecca Johnson, a nurse who heads the Research Center for Human/Animal Interaction at the University of Missouri College of Veterinary Medicine, "studies have focused on the fact that interacting with animals can increase people's level of the hormone oxytocin."

Oxytocin, a powerful hormone associated with pair bonding, acts as a neutrasmitter in the brain. This is the same hormone that helps new infants bond to their mothers.

"This is very beneficial for us," says Johnson. "Oxytocin helps us feel happy and trusting." Which, Johnson says, may be one of the ways that humans bond with their animals over time.

"Oxytocin also has some powerful effects for us in the body's ability to be in a state of readiness to heal and grow new cells," Johnson adds, "so it predisposes us to an environment in our own bodies where we can be healthier."

Living Single

Most people spend a good portion of their adult lives as single people, whether they're unmarried, divorced, or widowed. Despite progress in defining the individual with greater independence in today's society, there is still an emphasis on couples, as well as security in groups. If you've ever eaten at a table for one at a fine restaurant, you may know how it feels – people smile sympathetically or act like you're contagious, while waiters inquire, "Will someone else be joining you?"

Coupling is not the social solution to quality longevity for everyone. There are advantages to being single and having the flexibility to make decisions based on one's own needs and desires, without having to compromise to suit another person's whims. The need for social connectedness remains, however, and single people who maintain strong relationships with family, friends, and community groups live longer than those who do not. In fact, single women, who tend to have stronger and longer-lasting relationships with friends and family, outlive their male counterparts by several years. Single people can experience these benefits by remaining social and staying connected, whether it's through sports, work, dating, or other social activities.

Simple Ways to Take Part in the Community

- Take classes at adult education centers, community colleges, art schools, tai chi or yoga centers, community centers, ballroom dance halls, and more. You can meet others during the class or an after-class coffee while learning a new skill.

- Hobbies provide community through classes, clubs, associations, and mini-conventions. Even knitters have community events, such as "stitch and pitch" nights when fans bring their needles and yarn to a baseball game and root for the home team.

- Eating with others is also a great social endeavor. Set up regular monthly lunches with friends or a social group. Have potlucks or dinner parties, or arrange an ongoing restaurant tour of your favorite ethnic cuisine.

- Create a book club with friends or find one at a community college, religious organization, or library.

- Attend game nights. Some taverns have trivia nights, bookstores may have chess or board game nights, or you can invite friends to play Cranium®, Pictionary®, or Apples to Apples®. Games like these can make you laugh and create plenty of small talk.

- Join an association or community group for business, hobbies, or other interests. Many meetings of the chamber of commerce or small business owners offer introductory breakfasts or luncheons. Toastmasters also host events that help develop self-confidence in public speaking and connect you to others in meetings and speeches.

- Check out your local newspaper or community bulletin for events, meetings, and groups looking to connect.

- Go to a local school sporting event. Show your pride for the hometown, wear the school colors, and encourage area youth to give it their all.

Social Ties and Your Ageless Mind

"No man is an island," John Donne famously wrote. In recent years, neuroscientists have caught up with the wisdom of the 17th century poet in recognizing how important it is for us to stay connected and engaged with other people as we age.

Countless studies have shown that maintaining rich, meaningful relationships and social interaction is a key ingredient - along with exercise, nutrition, and lifelong learning - in the recipe for cognitive health. Those who make an effort to maintain close social bonds consistently show greater health and longevity, while those who remain isolated exhibit higher levels of congnitive decline.

As scientists gain ground in unlocking the mysteries of aging and longevity, we understand that we have some control over our cognitive and physical health - and that connecting with others is a vital way to protect both. Friends and family keep you healthy; and it is through these connections that you will be able to nurture and enjoy your ageless mind.

CHAPTER EIGHT

Music

> " *Music is moral law.*
> *It gives soul to the universe,*
> *wings to the mind, flight to the*
> *imagination, and charm and*
> *gaiety to everything.* "
>
> **Plato**

MUSIC AND THE BRAIN

Music is sensory, emotional, and motor – we feel the music, and it literally moves us. When music engages the brain – when performers play or listeners tap, dance, or sing along – the experience is often coupled with action.

Music is in our genes. At an early age our musical capacity is shaped by the culture in which we live. Our background influences the instruments we play, the songs that we sing, and even how we hear the notes. Music can enhance brain function, memory, and emotion. Music is powerful.

The brain is divided into two hemispheres. Typically, the right hemisphere has been identified as the seat of music, but there is not just one area in the brain responsible for music. In making and listening to music, we use both sides; music is an interplay of many functions. It is exactly for this reason that music is healing and has the ability to enhance brain function. Music integrates the entire brain.

Decoding Sound

When we hear music as well as speech or environmental noises, the brain has to decode the patterns in the sound before it can identify the sound. Complex sounds contain a number of elements that vary from frequency, time, loudness, and position. In music, for example, melody reflects patterns of sound pitches, while rhythm involves variation in the timing and duration of sounds. These patterns are processed in a series of brain regions between the *cochlea* (the auditory portion of the inner ear) and the high-level areas where the brain assigns a meaning to the sound or remembers where it was previously heard. "If I say the word 'dog', it's a pattern of sound but at another level it triggers a picture of a dog in your mind," says Dr. Tim Griffiths of Newcastle University. "Music and environmental sounds also have meanings associated with them, so we are working on the acoustic features of complex sounds that are important to us when processing particular types of information."

> **AGELESS MIND FACT**
>
> The cochlea acts quickly to begin processing sound, which travels at a speed of 1,130 feet per second, or about 770 miles per hour.

Healing Power of Music

Understanding the neuroscience of music allows us to harness its healing power. Studies have shown that following heart bypass surgery, patients in intensive care units where background music is played needed lower doses of drugs than patients in units where no music is played. Some hospitals play soft background music in intensive care units for premature babies. Such music, as well as a nurse's or a mother's humming, helps the premature babies gain weight faster and leave earlier than those who don't hear those sounds. At the other end of the spectrum, music has been used to calm Alzheimer's patients. Relaxed, soothing music has been shown to reduce confusion and irritability. In a University of Louisville Medical School study of retired nuns in two nursing homes, researchers introduced the playing of recorders and other instruments as the only change in the environment. They discovered significant improvements in memory; playing music, reading notes, and moving fingers all worked to enhance memory.

Music as Therapy

Researchers in Rome used music therapy as an additional treatment for severely brain-injured patients. The therapy consisted of musical improvisation between the patient and therapist by singing or by playing different musical instruments according to each patient's own unique abilities. In another study, doctors monitored thirty-four patients who had been in a coma for an average of fifty-two days. The results of these studies showed that the patients who had music therapy had a significant reduction of undesired behaviors such as inertia or agitation.

A daily dose of one's favorite pop melodies, classical music, or jazz can even speed recovery from debilitating strokes, according to the latest research. When stroke patients in Finland listened to music for a couple of hours each day, verbal memory and attention span improved significantly compared to patients who received no musical stimulation, or who listened only to stories read out loud.

Overall, music has been shown to have positive effects on physical healing and recovery. Today, music therapy is increasingly finding its way into hospitals to reduce the need for medication, to decrease postoperative pain, and even complement the use of anesthesia during surgery.

Music and Memory

For centuries, we have known that attaching information to music facilitates its recall. Dating back to the days when Medieval bards would provide the news of the day in song, music has long-provided a method to record and transfer information.

Many revealing scientific experiments, studies, and research projects have been performed to uncover the hidden power of music. Up until 1970, most of the research done on music had to do with studying the effects of the beat of the music. It was found that slow music could slow the heartbeat and the breathing rate as well as bring down blood pressure, while faster music was found to speed up these same body measurements.

The key component of music that makes it beneficial is order. The order of the music from the baroque and classical periods causes the brain to respond in special ways. This order includes repetition and changes, certain patterns of rhythm, and pitch and mood contrasts. One key ingredient to the order of music from the baroque and classical periods is math. The math may not be immediately realized by the body, but the human mind is designed to respond to patterns and, upon hearing them, reacts accordingly.

The Secret of Baroque Music

One shining example of the power of order in music is King George I of England. King George had big problems with memory loss and stress management. He read from the Bible the story of King Saul and recognized that Saul had experienced the same type of problems that he was experiencing. George recognized that Saul overcame his problems by using special music. With this in mind, King George asked George Frederick Handel to write some special music for him that would help him in the same way that music helped Saul. Handel wrote *Water Music* for this purpose.

The power of music to affect memory is quite intriguing. Research has shown that baroque music, written by Handel, Mozart, and others, follows a unique 60 beats-per-minute pattern that activates the left and right brain. Simultaneous left and right brain action maximizes learning and retention of information.

According to The Center for New Discoveries in Learning, learning potential can be increased a minimum of five times by incorporating 60 beats-per-minute music. A renowned Bulgarian psychologist, Dr. George Lozanov, designed a way, using baroque music, to teach foreign languages in a fraction of the normal learning time. In his system, students could learn up to one half of the vocabulary and phrases for the whole school term (which amounts to almost 1,000 words or phrases) in one day. Along with this, the average retention rate of his students was 92%. Combining baroque music with vocabulary retention, Dr. Lozanov also demonstrated that foreign languages can be learned with 85-100% efficiency in only thirty days. His students had a recall accuracy rate of almost 100% even after not reviewing the material for four years.

> **HEALTHY BRAIN TIP**
>
> For learning or memory use, it is best to choose music that doesn't have any vocals in it.

Music and the Heart

Music also has a well-recognized vascular component. Classical music from the baroque period causes the heart beat and pulse rate to relax to the beat of the music. As the body becomes relaxed and alert, the mind is able to concentrate more easily. Furthermore, baroque music decreases blood pressure and enhances the ability to learn. Music affects the amplitude and frequency of brain waves. Music also affects breathing rate and electrical resistance of the skin. It has been observed to cause the pupils to dilate, increase blood pressure, and increase the heart rate.

Singing

In Europe, patients with Parkinson's, Alzheimer's, and other neurological disorders are forming choirs to help strengthen their throat muscles. In New York and elsewhere, stroke patients are using melodies to facilitate their speech recovery. Researchers in Vancouver are exploring how music affects the brains of patients with bipolar disorder and depression.

For years, the psychological and spiritual benefits of singing have been universally recognized. From medical therapy to use in education, singing has long been a part of the human experience.

Singing as Therapy

There is a growing body of clinical evidence suggesting that singing can play a key role in improving motor function, communication, and even cognition for people with a broad range of brain-based conditions, including Alzheimer's disease, autism and Parkinson's disease. For example, melodic intonation therapy, in which vocal exercises are used to improve speech, has proven to be effective for patients with *aphasia*, a disorder that results from damage to portions of the brain responsible for language. Harvard researchers showed that singing seems to engage the brain's right hemisphere – which is involved with speech – and this may explain why melodic intonation therapy can also be an effective type of speech therapy for aphasia patients as well as those who have suffered a stroke.

> **HEALTHY BRAIN TIP**
>
> The benefits of singing are experienced despite personal ability... yes, even singing off-key in the shower counts!

Singing and Emotion

Singing may also help depressed people and allow them to express emotions. The National Institutes of Health states that the act of singing releases endorphins, increases the level of chemicals that build trust, and improves immune system response. Research by Canterbury Christ Church University found that singing improves mental health and wellbeing. According to professor Stephen Clift, "singing could potentially delay the onset of dementia and reduce depression." Researchers in Vancouver are also exploring how music affects the brains of patients with bipolar disorder and depression.

Singing and Education

Singing and music have long been connected to intelligence, creativity, emotions, and memory. When you put information to a tune, such as "The ABCs" (a Mozart piece), you are more likely to remember it. Singing stimulates temporal lobe function, an area of the brain heavily involved in memory. Preschool and kindergarten teachers have long used singing to enhance learning. Young military trainees sing as they march to build energy and morale. So why do we stop singing in the second or third grade? The next time you need to remember something important, try putting a little tune to it. You may be surprised at how much easier it will be to recall later.

Playing an Instrument

If you have always wanted to learn a musical instrument, now is the time. Learning to play a musical instrument enhances brain function. It teaches the brain new patterns and stimulates wide areas of the cortex. Music has the capacity to enhance the brain's ability to think, reason, and learn. The College Entrance Examination Board reported that students with experience in musical performance scored 51 points higher on the verbal part of the SAT and 39 points higher on the math section than the national average. In a study of approximately 7,500 students at a leading university, music majors had the highest reading scores of any students on campus. Music majors were also the most likely group of college grads to be admitted to medical school. Physician and biologist Lewis Thomas studied the undergraduate majors of medical school applicants. He found that 66% of music majors who applied to medical school were admitted – the highest percentage of any group. For comparison, 44% of biochemistry majors were admitted.

AGELESS MIND FACT

Besides its relationship with higher test scores, playing an instrument has also been linked to stress reduction and increased immunity.

Learning a musical instrument, at any age, can be helpful in developing and activating temporal lobe neurons. As the temporal lobes are activated in an effective way, they are more likely to improve brain function overall.

Two Men and a Violin

Many of the greatest minds in history were musicians. What most people don't realize, however, is what an influence their playing was in their own historic achievements. Here are two examples of how playing an instrument had an effect on the course of modern history.

1. Albert Einstein, one of the most brilliant minds in history, was an avid violinist. Einstein himself states that the reason he was so smart was because of his violin playing. Between his experiments, he would take time play his favorite music, preferring the classical works of Bach and Mozart. According to his friend, G.J. Withrow, the way Einstein figured out his problems and equations was by improvising on the violin.

2. The violin also helped American forefather Thomas Jefferson. Jefferson also played the violin and claimed that playing it helped him to write the Declaration of Independence. According to Jefferson, when he could not figure out the right wording for a certain part, he would play his violin to help him. The music helped get the words from his brain to the paper.

Music and Your Ageless Mind

Research conducted by Boston neurologist Gottfried Schlaug of Beth Israel Deaconess Medical Center suggests that playing a musical instrument can promote brain plasticity over a person's lifespan.

Dr. Schlaug, director of the Music and Neuroimaging Laboratory at Beth Israel, released a research paper in the medical trade magazine *The Neuroscientist* showing music's potential to suspend or counter the effects of aging.

Schlaug's research states that of the studies that have been conducted on the effect of music on the aging brain, the majority showed that musicians had more gray matter volume than non-musicians in specific areas of the brain.

"Thus, musicians appear to be less susceptible to age-related degenerations in the brain, presumably as a result of their daily musical activities," Schlaug wrote.

Schlaug pointed to another study in which participants 75 and older who played a musical instrument were less likely to have developed dementia of the course of a five-year research period.

"This protective effect of playing music was stronger than those of other cognitive activities such as reading, writing or doing crossword puzzles," he wrote.

Whether you are a singer, musician, or simply enjoy listening to your favorite songs, it seems that the positive effects of music are just what the doctor ordered for your ageless mind.

CHAPTER NINE

Lifelong Learning

" *Anyone who stops learning is old, whether at twenty or eighty. Anyone who keeps learning is young. The greatest thing in life is to keep your mind young.* "

Henry Ford

LIFELONG LEARNING

As 78 million Baby Boomers prepare to redefine their own retirement, news that staying active and keeping their brains constantly engaged may help stave off mental and physical ailments has many asking how best to do so. The answer is simple: lifelong learning. Lifelong learning is the continued educational experience that utilizes classes, educational travel, self-instruction, and community activity to fully engage the brain.

No other area is as rich in opportunity and promise for growth, excitement, and meaning as learning and education. For those now retired, education was seen as a young person's opportunity to acquire occupational or professional skills and competence. This is no longer true. Learning is now seen as a lifelong process, and education is something that many are now turning to in mid-life and later.

A New Era in Learning

Breaking out of old habits by embracing new learning opportunities is one of the simple secrets of revitalizing the mind. It is much easier to do this if you realize that the brain is designed to be the most profoundly powerful learning mechanism around.

Keep in mind that education does not have to be formal or structured in order to "count." There is an abundance of different ways to learn with endless benefits waiting to be realized. Depending on what stage of life you are in, what your financial needs are, and what kind of activities you value and enjoy, you will likely find yourself drawn to different learning opportunities. One thing is for sure: It is never too late to start.

"No matter how old you may be at this moment, it's never too late to change your brain for the better," states neuroscientist Richard Restak, MD. "That's because the brain is different from any other organ in the body. While the liver and lungs and the kidneys wear out after a certain number of years, the brain gets sharper the more it is used. Indeed it improves with use."

Protecting Against Alzheimer's Disease

Research has now shown that lifelong learning is directly related to the prevention of Alzheimer's disease. In a 2004 study, researchers at Rush University Medical Center in Chicago reported evidence in support of the connection between educational background and Alzheimer's disease symptoms. They examined relationships among the underlying Alzheimer's pathology at autopsy, years of education, and symptom severity in a group of elderly Catholic clergy who had been participants in a longitudinal study. They found that among people with similar levels of Alzheimer's disease pathology, those with higher levels of education exhibited fewer symptoms and better overall functioning.

The Nun Study

In 1986, a priceless treasure was discovered at the convent of the Sisters of Notre Dame in Mankato, Minnesota. The treasure was not precious stones or gold bars, but volumes of notes tucked away in an old file cabinet. The files were found by Dr. David Snowdon, a researcher on aging at the University of Minnesota. Buried in those pages were the essays that the then 21 year-old nuns had written as part of their entry into religious life.

The discovery led to a 10-year research project, now known as the "Nun Study," that followed the brain health of 678 sisters and compared their results against the essays they had each written decades earlier. During the study, the sisters submitted regularly to comprehensive examinations to show their patterns of aging and susceptibility of mental decline. Their final gift was that each had agreed to donate her brain to science upon death for use in further examination.

What Dr. Snowdon found would change the way we look at Alzheimer's disease. Some of the brains that were filled with Alzheimer's plaques and tangles belonged to women who showed no evidence of dementia, while others with lesser amounts had crippling cognitive impairment. Because of the essays and records that had been kept on these women, researchers could attribute some of the differences to education levels and lifelong learning.

The revelations of the Nun Study have shed light onto some of the darkest mysteries of the aging mind. For instance, the researchers found that certain traits of early adulthood could be used to predict the nuns' risk of developing Alzheimer's disease many decades later. Specifically, they identified that linguistic ability, as measured by the idea density and grammatical complexity of the early essays, is a good way to identify those at higher risk of mental decline. The women who had the lowest idea density and grammatical complexity in early adulthood also had the highest chance for poor intellectual performance and Alzheimer's disease in their later years. This finding suggests that a good linguistic ability in early adulthood can somehow protect brain degenerative disorders such as Alzheimer's disease. Since linguistic ability is known to be closely related to education, the researchers also examined the possible link between the number of years of formal schooling and the risk of memory problems. Similar to the finding for linguistic ability, the nuns who had more education were far more likely to maintain their intellectual capacity well into old age than were their counterparts who had fewer years of schooling.

Cognitive Reserve

What makes Dr. Snowdon's research so important to our understanding of Alzheimer's disease is the notion of *cognitive reserve.* Cognitive reserve is the brain's ability to store up cognitive ability that can supersede the effects of dementia and other brain impairments for a duration of time. Think of it like overdraft protection on your checking account. The Nun Study found that variables such as level of education and linguistic ability go directly to increasing that level of cognitive reserve. Study researchers also found support for the idea that the critical factor in cognitive reserve is not necessarily years of formal education, but rather ongoing participation in cognitively stimulating activities. They confirmed that people who more regularly engaged in cognitive activity were less likely to be diagnosed with dementia. Cognitive reserve appears to be malleable and dynamic, resulting from a combination of genetic factors and ongoing life experience.

Use It or Lose It

It's true that people with an advanced education appear to be at lower risk for memory disorders and age-related memory loss than people with less education. Even if you are among those with an advanced degree under your belt, do not forget that lifelong learning is just that - lifelong. Continue challenging yourself intellectually throughout life. Continuous learning is both a use-it-or-lose-it strategy for enriching life today and an investment in the future – helping to build up a cognitive reserve of neural connections. This reserve will help keep your memory and other cognitive functions sharp, even in the face of age-related changes in the brain.

Barriers to Learning

Despite its clear benefits, some people may find that they have barriers to overcome before taking advantage of educational opportunities. Some barriers are psychological. You might feel that education is for younger people - that you have already "paid your dues." If your earlier education was limited, you might have hesitations about your ability to learn and retain new things. Still others might feel awkward or embarrassed about trying something new.

Other barriers are more of a practical kind. You might, for example, have difficulty finding either the time or the transportation. You may also find, like many, that taking a class or investing in an expensive hobby is simply not in the budget.

Whatever may be standing in the way, just remember that there is a solution for every problem. Learning something new doesn't have to be expensive, uncomfortable, or even require you to leave the house. With today's technology and the capabilities of the internet, you can now learn an endless number of things right from the comfort of your own computer.

> **HEALTHY BRAIN TIP**
>
> Where can you go for free books, movies, workshops, and computer access? Your local library, of course - and many offer books online, too!

10 Easy Ways to Learn More

You don't need to go back to school to be a lifelong learner. Whether it is visiting a local museum or reading a good book, opportunities for learning are all around you. Here are some ideas to get you started.

1. Visit the local theatre, art gallery, or museum.

2. Plan and execute a do-it-yourself home improvement project.

3. Design and plant a new garden.

4. Volunteer for a project that involves a skill you don't normally use.

5. Delve into research on something that you've always been curious about.

6. Explore the internet. You can gain access to a wealth of information on any conceivable topic.

7. Join a book discussion group or particpate in a library program.

8. Join a chess, bridge, or poker club.

9. Take a course to learn a new skill that requires effort and practice, like playing a musical instrument, painting, or website design.

10. Sign up for a class at your local community center on subjects like ballroom dancing, cooking, or photography.

How to Approach the Learning Process

In school, most of us spent the majority of our time learning chemistry, mathematics, social studies, and other subjects. While many of us have had our fair share of these subjects, one area that might be worth repeating is how to learn. Here are some simple ideas that can help you enjoy learning more effectively.

- **Let go of the fear of embarrassment and failure.** The main impediment to adult learning is the fear of embarrassment and failure. Decide, as Susan Jeffers, PhD, counsels, to "feel the fear and do it anyway." Artist Georgia O'Keefe stated, "I've been absolutely terrified every moment of my life – and I've never let it keep me from doing a single thing I wanted to do."

- **Cultivate childlike curiosity.** The best way for adults to learn is to approach new learning experiences in an open, playful way, as children do. Make learning fun. Don't take anything, especially yourself, too seriously. As Irish playwright George Bernard Shaw explained, "We don't stop playing because we grow old; we grow old because we stop playing."

- **Embrace the process.** The process of learning something new is more important than the result. The benefit to your brain comes from the attempt to learn. A successful outcome is a bonus.

- **Seek new challenges.** Welcome change and keep trying new things. Benjamin Franklin cautioned, "When you're finished changing, you're finished." Get out of your old patterns. Take a watercolor painting class, try ballroom dancing, or sign up for singing lessons. Novelty yields brain effects. Neuroscientist Michael Merzenich, PhD, and his colleagues emphasize that learning a new skill can "change hundreds of millions" of neural connections.

- **Stretch your comfort zone.** You can accelerate your improvement by raising the degree of difficulty of your learning challenges: For example, try more complex crossword puzzles or play chess against a more advanced opponent. Marian Diamond, PhD, the world's leading neuroanatomist, observed that rats that ran through mazes without obstruction didn't demonstrate improvements in neural complexity, but rats that were challenged by having to climb over obstacles on the way to the proverbial cheese showed significant brain growth. Dr. Diamond argues that the same principle applies to humans. She writes, "Increase the level of environmental stimulation and you will increase the branching of dendrites and the thickness of the human cortex."

- **Invest fifteen minutes every day to new learning.** Neuroscientist Daniel G. Amen, MD, points out, "Spending just 15 minutes a day learning something new is all it takes for your brain to benefit from the activity."

- **Start today!** Begin learning something new today. You've probably noticed that as you get older, time seems to go faster. So whatever it is that you've always wanted to learn, begin it now. This will give you more time to enjoy the knowledge, and you'll be good at it before you realize it. Neuroscientist Marco Iacoboni, MD, PhD explains, "You can improve your mind as you age, and now is the best time to begin."

Learning memory systems, mental sports, new languages, new vocabulary, and juggling are all wonderful ways to maintain a vibrant, lively mind. Other especially beneficial activities include dance, creative writing, tai chi, cooking, drawing, and becoming computer and web savvy. Although these activities offer special benefits, the greatest benefit probably accrues from your engagement of any activity that is new and challenging. As neuroscientist Daniel G. Amen, MD, emphasizes, "New learning actually causes new connections to form in your brain. It has a positive effect on your brain and can help keep you young. The best mental exercise is acquiring new knowledge and doing things you haven't done before."

> **AGELESS MIND FACT**
> MRI scans of people who learned to juggle showed a growth of gray matter after completing a 6-week class.

Reasons for more education

Studies for a Second Career

If you wish to pursue a second career, it might be necessary to get additional education. Before committing to a lengthy degree or certification program, you would do well to enlist the services of a career planning expert. Inquire at your nearest community college about career development programs such as classes, workshops, seminars, or individual counseling.

Depending on the area you pursue, you might need a certificate or degree. Maybe you would like to go back to an interrupted career, such as teaching, and will need accreditation. If starting a business is your goal, no degree is necessary, but you might benefit from taking courses in business-related subjects, such as accounting, contracts, or marketing, or simply to learn more about the business you are considering.

There are ways to fashion viable second careers if you are willing to learn some of the in's and out's. For example, you might offer consultation services in an area where you have expertise, or you could promote your marketable skills in the areas of computers or accounting.

Useful Knowledge

Pastimes such as maintaining our homes and enjoying our hobbies will be easier if we learn the best way to do them. For instance, do you like to refinish furniture? Do you want to reupholster the sofa? Is the wallpaper in your bathroom in need of replacement? Have you harbored a desire to learn how to sew? Would you like to learn the basics of a foreign language so you can communicate with the locals when traveling to a foreign country? What about learning money management skills? Do you want to better understand health and nutrition for older people? There is likely to be a course on anything you wish to learn.

Fun and Pleasure

Certain learning experiences are stimulating and open our minds to new vistas and perspectives of life and the world. Courses in the arts, literature, music, or any number of humanities programs afford personal growth. You might work for a degree in something just for the fun of it, or take specific classes that interest you. These opportunities will broaden your outlook on life, possibly satisfying a thirst for understanding and awareness that you could not respond to years earlier. Hobby courses provide useful knowledge that overlaps with pleasure. Learning is often fun, and many find it a pleasurable activity in itself.

Learning Opportunities

Instruction in an array of subjects is offered in various education settings, and much of it is free or discounted for older adults. You will find courses on just about everything in universities, community colleges, trade schools, museums, senior centers, and libraries. These are often listed under Adult Education in course catalogs.

Many community colleges offer courses for credit over public television channels. For those of you with access to a computer, many educational programs are available on disks, and the internet is a vast source of information.

Thanks to legislation enacted during the sixties and seventies, support for a wide variety of programs is available for older adults. In most states, universities and colleges have policies that waive tuition for people over sixty or sixty-five. Such tuition waivers depend on space availability in classes or may limit participation to auditing classes (taking courses without earning credit). Some programs are specifically designed for seniors.

Other sources include craft stores, which will furnish information about arts and crafts courses and presentations. Health organizations such as hospitals often hold conferences and consultations with training. Some organizations present interesting speakers on various subjects at their meetings. Libraries, continuing education programs, senior centers, and museums are also valuable resources. Some bookstores feature readings by published authors. Everywhere you look, a learning opportunity is waiting to be discovered.

College for Adults

Just because you're no longer a kid doesn't mean your college days are over. Those who miss carting a backpack filled with textbooks and freshly sharpened pencils around campus—but don't miss the tuition—can take free or low-cost classes at many colleges and universities. In some cases, you'll have to meet age, residency, and income restrictions. With a little research, you just might find yourself writing term papers again. Here's a guide to spending your retirement years on campus without worrying about student loans:

Tuition Waivers

Approximately 60% of accredited degree-granting educational institutions offer tuition waivers for older adults, according to a November 2008 survey by the American Council on Education. A typical offering is the University of Delaware's Higher Education for Senior Citizens, which includes free tuition for degree candidates who are Delaware residents and age 60 or older (the university still charges a variety of fees, however.) Colleges that don't offer tuition waivers sometimes provide tuition discounts to seniors.

Audit a Course

Taking college courses on an audit basis means attending lectures without the homework and exams. Florida residents age 60 or older may audit classes through the Senior Citizen Tuition Fee Waiver program, but they won't receive college credit. Even if your state doesn't have an official audit program or tuition wavier, it's worth asking if you can sit in on a class that interests you. Auditing arrangements are often made on an individual basis.

Community College

According to the American Council on Education, about half of college-going adults age 50 and older attend community colleges, primarily for fun, to connect with other people, and to retool for a new career. As many as 84% of community colleges offer courses specifically for students age 50 and older, according to a recent survey of community colleges by the American Association of Community Colleges (AACC). While not free, community colleges can provide classes at a lower cost than their larger university competitors.

Scholarships for Seniors

While many scholarships are aimed at traditional undergraduates, it's worth reading the fine print if you think you might be eligible. Also, be on the lookout for scholarship programs just for seniors. For example, the state of Alabama has a Senior Adults Scholarship Program that provides free tuition for senior citizens age 60 and over, and Northern Michigan University offers a full tuition scholarship for applicants age 62 and older.

Classes for Seniors

Some colleges offer continuing education classes specifically for adults age 50 and older. The courses typically last a few weeks instead of an entire semester. There is also a network of Osher Lifelong Learning Institutes at approximately 120 colleges and universities in the U.S., including California Polytechnic State University, Texas Tech University, and the University of South Florida. These courses are for adults who don't want papers or exams, and the fees vary considerably by program. At George Mason, for example, the fees range from $125 to $350 annually for an unlimited number of courses over four semesters.

Online Courses

Many well-known universities such as MIT, Stanford, and Yale allow anyone to audit select courses online free of charge. Other colleges wave online course fees for state residents above a certain age. For example, seniors age 65 and older in North Carolina can take public university courses in person, online, or through correspondence for credit without paying tuition. "The online courses are pretty neat because you don't have to leave the house," says Peter Rizzolo, 80, a retired doctor who has taken classes both online and in person at the University of North Carolina at Chapel Hill and North Carolina State University on topics including American history, art, and Italian. "I've gotten literally thousands of dollar worth of credits - 120 or so - for free," he says. "All I've paid for is my books and lab fees for courses like astronomy."

Lifelong Learning and Your Ageless Mind

The benefits of learning and education for older people are many. Continued learning has been demonstrated to have a positive effect on maintaining intellectual functioning into old age. Learning also helps increase self-esteem and affords a feeling of achievement. As a lifelong learner you will look at the world with more curiosity and interest – a crucial attitude for finding meaning in life.

There are many different ways, both formal and informal, to engage in lifelong learning and to build up cognitive reserve. Through educational opportunities, we are able to develop our natural abilities, immerse ourselves in the wonders of life, increase our wisdom, and empower ourselves to make the world a better place.

In the words of Dr. Paul Nussbaum, Director of the Aging Research and Education Center in Pittsburgh, PA, "Every time your heart beats, 25% of that blood goes right to the brain. But while exercise is critical, it may be education that is more important. In the 21st century, education and information have become for the brain what exercise is for the heart."

Just like the human heart, our brains need to be nurtured. If so, then lifelong learning can be considered a health club for your ageless mind.

Your Ageless Nutrition

We all know that a healthy diet can help us stay slim, but research now shows that good eating habits can help preserve memory, improve mood, and support neuroplasticity. They can also reduce the risk of chronic age-related brain diseases such as Alzheimer's and dementia. Nutrition plays a large part in brain development and function throughout life. In these final chapters, we will discuss both the good and bad of nutrition, as well as provide strategies and recipes to give you a head start.

CHAPTER TEN

Brain Food

" *I do not like broccoli. And I haven't liked it since I was a kid and my mom made me eat it. And I'm President of the United States and I'm not going to eat broccoli anymore.* "

George H. W. Bush

HEALTHY BRAIN NUTRITION

Nutrition is the most important tool for staying mentally and physically fit, and it is by far the most underutilized tool.

Scientists are just beginning to fully understand the strong links between nutrition and mental function, and how it alters memory, concentration, and cognitive performance. Just as a good stew is composed of many ingredients, brain food is an assortment of healthy nutrients. Poor food choices directly impact mental health and longevity by potentially increasing the risk of Alzheimer's disease, heart disease, and other age-related illnesses.

Dining on foods that are rich in antioxidants, healthy fats, and whole grains, while avoiding foods that trigger inflammation, such as trans fats and refined carbs, help the brain stay in shape. Let's take a closer look at these healthy brain choices.

Rust-proofing your Brain and Body

If you leave a bottle of wine open too long, it will oxidize and become stale. If your car hasn't received the appropriate protective coating, it may rust over time. Just as wine degrades and metal rusts, so it is with the body and the brain. Over the years, your system generates chemicals known as free radicals that have the effect of oxidizing, or "rusting," your cells.

A **free radical** is an unstable molecule – a molecule short of a needed electron. This molecule roams around your system looking to grab an electron from healthy molecules in order to stabilize itself. Stealing an electron from a previously stable molecule makes that second molecule unstable, which then avidly seeks stabilization, thus perpetrating a chain reaction of molecular destruction that exacerbates symptoms associated with unhealthy aging.

Free-radical scavengers, known as antioxidants, can counter the destructive effects of free radicals by effectively quenching their desire for additional electrons, thus rendering them harmless. Nutritionists at the National Institute on Aging in Bethesda, Maryland, have created a rating scale for the antioxidant level of various foods according to "oxygen radical absorption capacity, or "ORAC." Enjoy foods with high ORAC ratings for the greatest "rust-proofing" effect. The following are some delicious recommendations.

- **Live a Fruitful Life.** Cranberries, plums, blackberries, raspeberries, and blueberries all have strong antioxidant benefits. Other fruits that serve as free-radical scavengers include pears, apples, peaches, pomegranates, oranges, kiwis, grapefruit, and red grapes. Red grapes contain high levels of the potent antioxidants and is partly why moderate enjoyment of red wine can be beneficial to your health. Dried fruits, including prunes, dates, and apricots, can also be high in antioxidants. Check the labels before buying dried fruits to be sure there are no preservatives, added sugar, or other unnecessary additives.

- **Eat Your Vegetables.** Broccoli, cabbage, sweet potatoes, Brussels sprouts, spinach, kale, carrots, chili peppers, bell peppers, parsley, asparagus, avocados, zucchini, beets, peas, artichokes, onions, and romaine lettuce contain a variety of wonderfully effective antioxidant components. The antioxidant benefits of these vegetables are usually enhanced by cooking. A review, by Gladys Block, PhD of more than two hundred nutritional studies concluded that those who regularly ate more vegetables and fruit than average were significantly less vulnerable to cancer and heart disease.

- **Add Garlic.** Garlic is one of the most healthful ingredients you can enjoy in your daily diet. Garlic's benefits as an antioxidant, antibacterial, antifungal agent are well documented. It also helps to maintain healthy cholesterol levels, reduce blood pressure, and promote good circulation.

- **Eat Beans.** Beans are high in antioxidants and fiber. Among the best are black, red, broad, kidney, and pinto.

- **Go Nuts (and Seeds).** Nuts and seeds are another rich source of antioxidants, especially pistachios, almonds, pecans, walnuts, hazelnuts, and sunflower seeds.

- **Add Spice to Your Life.** These spices and herbs add more flavor to your food, and they all offer a powerful antioxidant effect: cumin, cloves, cinnamon, turmeric, mustard, ginger, oregano, basil, sage, thyme, and tarragon.

- **Experience Wholeness (through Grains and Cereal).** Barley, millet, oats, and corn are all loaded with vitamin E, a powerful antioxidant that helps prevent cancer by supporting the immune system. Studies also suggest that vitamin E helps prevent arthritis and may lessen the likelihood of Alzheimer's. A recent report from the American Society of Nutrition symposium states, "Current scientific evidence indicates that whole grains play an important role in lowering the risk of chronic diseases, diabetes, and cancer, and also contribute to body weight management and gastrointestinal health."

- **Enjoy Teatime.** The world's most popular drink is also one of the healthiest. White, green, and black teas are all rich in antioxidants. Regular enjoyment of tea is a simple and refreshing way to help ward off a wide range of ailments.

Fighting Inflammation

Inflammation is one of the first responses of the immune system, which is the body's defense mechanism that protects us from infections, foreign bodies, and other physical threats. When the immune system is not properly functioning, we are more susceptible to bacterial or viral infections.

As scientists continue to figure out how the body ages, they are discovering that chronic inflammation is a driving force of many age-related illnesses – not only cancer and heart disease, but also Alzheimer's disease. When our body's immune system is working correctly, it helps the body heal from injuries.

Lack of sleep, stress, toxins such as smoke, and a sedentary lifestyle all contribute to chronic inflammation. The good news is that nutritional scientists are discovering many foods that can help our bodies control inflammation and protect brain health. Some studies have indicated that a low-calorie diet can alter the expression of inflammatory genes in fat tissue. In other words, the number of calories we eat each day can have a direct effect on the DNA in fat cells. Ingesting fewer calories turns on anti-inflammatory genes to help control chronic inflammation.

Many of the healthiest brain foods, including fruits, vegetables, fish, whole grains, and legumes fight inflammation. Spices and aromatic herbs also have anti-inflammatory effects and may boost immune function. In addition, the flavonoids found in colorful fruits and vegetables have also been found to protect the body from chronic inflammation.

More Antioxidants

Eating antioxidant foods may protect our brains from oxidative free radicals that cause wear and tear on the DNA in our cells. Colorful berries, such as strawberries, blackberries, and blueberries contain polyphenols that fight oxidants. Other antioxidant foods containing polyphenols include grapes, pears, plums, cherries, broccoli, cabbage, celery, onions, and parsley.

The Rotterdam Study, in the Netherlands, reported that an increased dietary intake of the antioxidant vitamin E was associated with a lower risk of developing Alzheimer's disease. In another large-scale European study of more than 8,000 volunteers age 65 and older, daily consumption of fruits and vegetables was associated with decreased risk of all causes of dementia.

AGELESS MIND FACT

Blueberries, besides being great antioxidants, also contain healthy minerals like copper, iron, potassium, manganese, and zinc.

In numerous scientific studies, low levels of antioxidants in the blood are associated with memory impairment, and laboratory animals fed antioxidant-rich berry extracts show better short-term memory (measured by how well they find their way through mazes). Other studies seem to support the belief that people who eat antioxidant fruits and vegetables have a lower risk for developing Alzheimer's disease.

Nutritional scientists use a standard measure that determines a food's ability to fight oxidation. As described earlier, the ORAC score provides a general indication of the ability of a particular food to protect brain cells from the damaging bombardment of free radicals. Most people eat only about 1,000 ORAC units a day, yet some experts recommend a daily dose closer to 3,500 units for optimal brain protection.

The table that follows is based on laboratory measurements from the U.S. Department of Agriculture and lists examples of some fruits and vegetables ranked according to their antioxidant potency.

Antioxidant Potency ORAC Units per 3½ ounces

Fruits	Vegetables
Cranberries - 9,100	Garlic - 5,700
Prunes - 8,100	Red Cabbage - 2,500
Plums - 7,600	Sweet Potato (w/ skin) - 2,100
Blackberries - 5,900	Broccoli - 2,100
Raspberries - 4,700	Beets - 1,800
Blueberries - 4,700	Radishes - 1,700
Pomegranates - 4,500	Spinach - 1,500
Strawberries - 4,300	Red onions - 1,500
Apples (granny smith) - 3,900	Yellow onions - 1,200
Raisins - 3,400	Romaine lettuce - 1,000

It is recommended that you eat a wide range of these foods, since each fruit and vegetable has its own unique nutrient profile. You can get an antioxidant boost by eating fruits and vegetables in a salad or snack, taking an antioxidant supplement, or drinking fruit and vegetable juices. Investigators from Vanderbilt School of Medicine, in Nashville, Tennessee, found that drinking fruit or vegetable juice at least three times a week compared with less than once a week lowered the risk for developing Alzheimer's disease.

The Magic of Pomegranate Juice

Researchers at UCLA showed that drinking pomegranate juice may provide an extra boost of brain power. A study followed people aged 50 to 75 (average age 64) who had mild memory complaints associated with aging. Half the group drank an 8-ounce glass of pomegranate juice each day, while the other half drank 8 ounces of a placebo drink that had the color and taste of pomegranate juice. After testing the recall abilities of both groups, the pomegranate group had significantly better scores. They also found that the pomegranate group showed a different pattern of brain activity while playing a video game that required memory for places – the regions controlling visual and memory functions showed greater levels of activity.

Studies of small animals with the human Alzheimer's gene have demonstrated similar brain-boosting benefits from pomegranate juice. Experimental Alzheimer's mice that drank pomegranate juice for six months had significantly better memory ability when finding their way through their mazes compared to those drinking the placebo. The juice-drinking mice also had fewer amyloid plaques in their brains.

AGELESS MIND FACT

Thomas Jefferson planted pomegranate trees at his Monticello home in 1771.

Most of us don't consume enough fruits and vegetables, and upping our servings is good not only for the brain but for the rest of the body, too. If you're concerned about the extra calories from raisins or prunes, green tea is another good source of antioxidants, and its phytochemicals have antiamyloid and anti-inflammatory properties as well. Choosing the right antioxidant vegetables will satiate those hunger pangs and help with weight control: Eight ounces of your favorite green vegetable can fill you up more than your favorite processed cookie. Tomatoes contain a strong antioxidant known as lycopene, so V-8® and tomato juice are also good antioxidant options. Fresh is not the only way – frozen berries maintain their antioxidant power and make great healthy snacks.

Proteins: Getting to the Meat of It

An Alzheimer's prevention diet combines healthy nutrition from a variety food groups, and protein is an essential component. In their study of food combinations and Alzheimer's risk, Columbia University researchers found that diets emphasizing proteins from fish and vegetables can lower the risk of Alzheimer's disease compared with diets combining red meat and butter and lower amounts of fruits and vegetables.

Eating a carbohydrate snack — such as an apple or a bag of pretzels — makes us feel satisfied for a while, but soon afterward we tend to feel hungry again. Adding a protein to the snack, perhaps a cup of nonfat yogurt, will provide longer-lasting appetite satisfaction, so we can better control hunger and body weight.

Amino acids are the building blocks of all proteins, which also provide the structure for the body's enzymes that maintain normal cellular function. Nine of the 20 amino acids that our bodies need are ***essential amino acids***. We call them essential because the body cannot synthesize them, or make them on its own: We can only get them though our diet. Fish, poultry, meat, eggs, milk, yogurt, cheese, and soybeans all contain the nine essential amino acids.

Fish - The Other White "Meat"

Fish is not only a great source of omega-3 fats but it also provides healthy protein. The American Heart Association recommends eating fish twice a week. Wild salmon, halibut, light tuna, cod, flounder, sole, sea bass, shrimp, lobster, scallops, and crab are all healthy choices. Keep in mind that farmed fish has generally more total fat than fish caught in the wild. Also, too much fish can increase mercury levels in the blood. Larger predatory fish such as shark and swordfish contain proportionately more mercury than smaller fish like salmon or sole.

What if you don't like fish? White meat chicken and lean beef make healthy entrée choices, too. The following is a list of healthy protein options.

Healthy Protein Options

- Beef – lean cuts
- Chicken breast
- Cheese – low-fat or non-fat cottage cheese, cream (light), goat, mozzarella, ricotta, and low-fat Swiss
- Eggs, egg whites
- Fish – anchovy, halibut, herring, salmon, trout, sea bass, tuna, whitefish, tilapia, and sardines
- Milk – low-fat, non-fat (skim)
- Nuts – almonds, walnuts, and peanuts
- Nut butter – almond
- Soy proteins – tofu, edamame
- Turkey breast
- Yogurt – low-fat or nonfat

Eat Brain-Friendly Carbohydrates

Compared with the rest of the body, our brains require a considerable amount of energy, and carbohydrates provide a major source of that energy. Whole-grain and high-fiber foods are brain healthy and help control weight, lower blood pressure, prevent strokes, and reduce the risk for diabetes and heart disease. The body takes longer to digest whole grains and high fiber foods than processed foods. Examples of whole grains include 100 percent whole grain bread, brown rice, oatmeal, and even popcorn. Eating whole grains and fresh fruit helps people feel more full while eating fewer calories.

In processed foods, some of the vitamins, minerals, and phytonutrients have been removed. Food processing also removes the fiber from carbohydrates, which increases the food's *glycemic index*. Carbohydrates are made up of sugar, or glucose, and after digesting a meal, the glucose is transported from the digestive tract to the blood. The glycemic index, or GI, ranges from 0 to 100 and classifies carbohydrates according to how quickly they raise blood sugar levels.

Most processed foods, including sugared cereals, cookies, crackers, and instant foods, have high GI ratings. Because they are digested and absorbed rapidly, these high-GI foods spike blood sugar levels quickly. Foods with low GI ratings, such as vegetables, fresh fruits, nonfat plain yogurt, soybeans, and nuts, are digested slowly, resulting in a slower blood sugar rise, which is healthier and keeps us satisfied longer. Research suggests that a low GI diet may decrease the risk of developing diabetes.

Investigators from the Cooper Institute in Dallas, Texas, studied more than 10,000 volunteers and found that a low glycemic diet can reduce the risk of metabolic syndrome. That's good news for brain health because metabolic syndrome increases the risk of heart disease, diabetes, and Alzheimer's disease.

Dark Chocolate for Health and Romance

It's more than wishful thinking - chocolate can actually be good for you. Packed with natural antioxidants, dark chocolate sits in the same category as green tea and blueberries. But that's only the beginning of its benefits.

1. Eating dark chocolate can raise alertness and temporarily improve performance in a range of cognitive tasks, according to a presentation given to the American Association for the Advancement of Science by Ian MacDonald, PhD. MacDonald's report is one of an increasing number of scientific studies demonstrating the benefits of moderate consumption of high-quality dark chocolate.

2. In addition to the health benefits, chocolate is a reliable source of enjoyment. Dark chocolate induces the release of endorphins, which are associated with feelings of pleasure; it also contains serotonin, a chemical that acts as an antidepressant. Perhaps that's why chocolate lovers often experience chocolate as a substitute for (or complement to) romance.

Eliminate Unnecessary Sugar

Alright - you can have your chocolate without feeling guilty. But how much is too much? Americans consume an average of 150 pounds of sugar per person per year, according to <u>Suicide by Sugar</u>, co-authored by clinical nutritionist Nancy Appleton. The book explains how over-consumption of sugar contributes to many disorders, from obesity and diabetes to depression and Alzheimer's disease. An overdose of sugar raises insulin levels in a way that can suppress the immune system, thereby increasing vulnerability to these and other ailments. Excess sugar also feeds inflammation throughout the body. Eliminating unnecessary sugar is difficult because it is a common ingredient in many foods, including a surprising number of so-called health foods. A recent trip to a natural foods store revealed "concentrated cane juice" (that is, sugar) in products ranging from chicken broth and frozen pizza to flaxseed waffles and beets. When heading out to the grocery store, keep an eye out for the many "disguises" of sugar.

Common "Disguises" of Sugar

- Corn syrup
- Cane sugar
- Glucose
- Fructose
- Maltodextrin
- Malt syrup
- Sorbitol

Unnecessary sugar dulls the palate and contributes wasted calories to your diet. It is one reason that obesity is increasingly widespread. You will need to be vigilant to eliminate this unhealthy influence from your diet.

Tereza Hubkova, MD, an expert in healthy aging and a physician at the renowned Canyon Ranch Health Resort, explains, "Glucose (sugar) binds to the proteins in our arteries (and elsewhere) creating something called advanced glycosylated end-products – the abbreviation for which is AGE. This pretty much sums up what excess sugar does to your organs, including the brain."

Spice it Up

Spices and herbs add color and flavoring to foods and can provide a healthy alternative to salt. Although only small amounts are generally used in cooking and seasoning, they add potential health benefits through their antioxidants and other effects. For example, consuming garlic lowers cholesterol levels and blood pressure, ginger may lessen pain in patients with arthritis, and several herbs and spices are believed to have cancer-fighting properties.

The following list illustrates the strong antioxidant potencies of several herbs and spices measured in quantities of three and a half ounces. All of these spices provide antioxidant benefits, even in single recipe amounts, so it's a good idea to vary your spices rather than emphasize any particular one.

Antioxidant Potency ORAC Units per 3½ ounces

Spices	
Oregano, dried - 25,000	Cumin seed - 7,700
Cinnamon, ground - 18,800	Curry powder - 6,900
Turmeric, ground - 18,200	Ginger, ground - 5,600
Vanilla bean, dried - 17,500	Pepper, black - 4,900
Parsley, dried - 10,500	Chili powder - 3,400
Basil, dried - 8,700	Paprika, ground - 3,250

Scientists have also studied piperine, the main antioxidant ingredient in black pepper. After just two weeks, the piperine not only improved memory performance in experimental mice that carried an Alzheimer's gene, but also delayed neurodegeneration in the hippocampus memory center of their brains.

Maintaining Healthy Hydration

Water is essential for life. It is also critical for brain health. The amount of water you ingest every day depends on a range of factors, including activity level, weight, the relative humidity in the environment, and your general health. The average recommended amount is eight to ten eight-ounce glasses of pure water daily. You can complement your water intake by enjoying plenty of fresh fruits and vegetables with high water content.

Avoiding Dehydration

Dehydration is a common cause, or a factor, in a range of ailments, from headaches to joint pain. Dehydration also raises cortisol and other stress hormone levels, thereby interfering with clarity of thought and memory acuity. It's a sneaky condition - most folks aren't aware that they are suffering from some degree of dehydration. Although thirst is a reliable sign that you need more hydration, you may need it even if you don't feel thirsty - so make it a habit of drinking water throughout the day. Dr. Daniel G Amen explains, "Proper hydration is the first rule of good nutrition. Even slight dehydration increases the body's stress hormones, which can decrease your ability to think clearly... (and) are associated with memory problems."

Alcohol and caffeine both have a dehydrating effect on the brain and body, so drink extra water in proportion to your enjoyment of wine and coffee. Avoid drinking anything that contains artificial sweeteners, added sugar, or chemical additives. Pure water is the best liquid to drink throughout the day, every day.

Dehydration Cause Brain Shrinkage

Failing to drink enough water can make your grey matter shrink, making it harder to think, experts have warned. Research shows that dehydration not only affects the size of the brain but also how it works. Just 90 minutes of steady sweating can shrink the brain as much as a year of aging, researchers believe. Starved of water, the grey matter is also forced to work harder to process the same information.

Over days and weeks, lack of fluid could impact performance at work and school. This negative impact can be quickly corrected, however, as a glass or two of water can return the brain back to normal levels.

Caffeine

Moderate drinking of caffeinated beverages does, however, offer its own benefits. A large-scale epidemiological study from Sweden reported that drinking up to three cups of coffee a day was associated with a 65% lower rate of developing Alzheimer's disease. A daily dose of coffee also lowers the risk of Parkinson's disease and diabetes, two age-related conditions that increase the risk for dementia.

A cup or two of joe also appears to protect the brain from the harmful effects of cholesterol. University of North Carolina scientists reported that when laboratory animals were fed diets high in cholesterol they found leaks in their blood-brain barriers, the natural shields that protect the brain from blood toxins. The mice that ingested daily coffee had much sturdier blood-brain barriers, preventing more cholesterol from entering into their brains.

Short-term mental effects of caffeine can be both positive and negative. Caffeine makes us more alert, increases attention, and elevates mood. Studies of learning and recall demonstrate short-term improvements following coffee consumption. Too much caffeine, however, can make us irritable and anxious and can lead to insomnia, especially when consumed in the evening. If you drink coffee every day, you're likely to experience caffeine withdrawal if you go without. As many of us know, the headache and lethargy from caffeine withdrawal is quite unpleasant. Keep in mind that caffeine is present in many foods and beverages. A six-ounce cup of coffee contains 100 milligrams, a carbonated cola has 45 milligrams, a cup of tea has 40 milligrams, and a chocolate bar has about 10 milligrams. As we age, we become more sensitive to the effects of caffeine. People who are particularly sensitive to caffeine should know that even an after-lunch espresso can have a disruptive effect on sleep later in the night.

A Toast to Your Brain Health

For years now we've known about the association of consuming red wine in moderation and having a lower risk for developing Alzheimer's disease. Too much alcohol, however, is harmful to the brain, and just how much is "too much" varies according to the particular study. Some studies suggest that one glass of wine is brain protective for women and two glasses are the healthy limit for men. The difference may reflect the fact that men are usually larger than women and can tolerate more alcohol.

Wine drinkers may benefit from an additional healthy brain compound found in grapes called *resveratrol*, which increases the lifespan of animals in a way that is similar to caloric restriction.

Scientists at Mount Sinai School of Medicine in New York studied the effects of wine on experimental laboratory mice that possessed a human Alzheimer's gene. They found that when the mice ingested moderate amounts of cabernet sauvignon wine – the mouse equivalent of a six-ounce glass – the animals had better memory ability and less of the protein that forms the building blocks of amyloid plaques in the brain.

Curtis Ellison, MD, an epidemiologist and wine lover, has dedicated a considerable amount of time and energy reviewing the literature on the health effects of wine. He told *Wine Spectator Magazine*, "Moderate wine consumption can safely add pleasure to your life and reduce our risks of falling prey to many of the most common health hazards of contemporary life, including heart disease, stroke, dementia, and even obesity."

Researchers have conducted many studies on the potential health benefits of wine that support Dr. Ellison's optimism. The most reliable and significant findings all focus on the potential benefits of regular, moderate red wine consumption. Reported benefits include a reduced risk of prostate and other forms of cancer, a decreased incidence of type 2 diabetes, a reduced risk of cardiovascular and coronary disease, and the prevention of Alzheimer's disease and other forms of dementia.

Brain Food for Your Ageless Mind

Food is powerful medicine.

We all know that eating a nutritious diet can help us stay slim, but overwhelming evidence now shows that healthy brain foods can also preserve memory, support brain function, and have the potential to reduce our risk of chronic age-related brain hazards such as Alzheimer's and dementia.

In this chapter, we learned about the powerful benefits that can be experienced after making simple changes to our diet. By making an effort to consume more brain-healthy foods like lean proteins, rich spices, and high-antioxidant fruits and vegetables, we can help protect our brain and body against inflammation and disease.

Current research into diet and brain health has shown that nutrition plays a large part in brain development and function throughout life. With good nutrition and healthy eating habits, you can be on your way to reducing the risk of future ailments and improving day-to-day mental health and well being.

So enjoy a bit of dark chocolate once in awhile, but remember to eliminate the excess sugars, limit the caffeine, stay well-hydrated, and raise a glass of red wine for a toast to you and your ageless mind.

CHAPTER ELEVEN

Fats

> *I will never use a substitute for butter. Margarine is one molecule away from eating plastic. If I'm going to eat that type of food, it's going to be the real deal*
>
> **Paula Deen**

FATS AND YOUR BRAIN

Fats are vital to a healthy diet. They help carry, absorb, and store the fat-soluble vitamins (A, D, E, and K) in the bloodstream. Fats also help regulate body temperature and cushion the organs, protecting them from injury.

Approximately 60 percent of the brain matter consists of fats. Fats are needed to create cell membranes throughout the brain and body. If your diet is loaded with bad fats, your brain can only make low-quality nerve cell membranes that don't function well; if your diet provides the essential, good fats, your brain cells can manufacture higher-quality nerve cells that function at peak capacity.

The fats that provide healthy support to the brain and body are called **fatty acids**. "Essential" fatty acids are those fats that cannot be manufactured in the body and must be fund in the foods we eat or from supplements. Fatty acids are used to produce hormone-like substances that regulate a wide range of functions, including blood pressure, blood clotting, blood lipid levels, the immune response, and the inflammation response to injury or infection.

Fatty acids serve different purposes in the body. They may:

- Be burned for energy.
- Form structures for your cell membranes.
- Create steroids and cholesterol.
- Perform special duties in nerve cells and other tissues.

It is important to choose foods that offer the essential fatty acids the body and brain need. As you already know, however, there are good fats... and then there are bad fats.

4 Types of Fat

There are four primary categories of fat in the foods we eat: monounsaturated fat and polyunsaturated fat (often called "good" fats), and saturated fat and trans-fatty acids (often called "bad" fats). The first three types occur naturally in food. The fourth kind, trans-fatty acid, is a creation of modern chemical processing and has found its way into the food supply, and into your brain.

Monounsaturated Fat

Monosunsaturated fat (MUFA) is a brain-friendly fat. It is found in common cooking oils, including olive oil, canola oil, and some forms of safflower oil, nuts, and avocados. Naturally high in antioxidants, monounsaturated fats are subject to less oxidative damage than other types of fat. That means that when they become incorporated into brain cells, they are less vulnerable to free radical attack, which means they are less prone to damage.

These relatively stable fats are better than polyunsaturated fats, but less stable than saturated fats. They solidify in the fridge, but are liquid at room temperature.

Studies show that eating foods rich in monounsaturated fats improve blood cholesterol levels, which can decrease the risk of heart disease. Research also shows that MUFAs may benefit insulin levels and blood sugar control, which can be especially helpful if you have type 2 diabetes.

Sources of Monounsaturated Fat

- Olive Oil
- Canola Oil
- Sunflower Oil
- Peanut Oil
- Sesame Oil
- Avocados
- Olives
- Nuts (almonds, cashews, hazelnuts, pecans, peanuts, macadamia nuts)
- Peanut Butter

Polyunsaturated Fat

Some forms of polyunsaturated fat (PUFA) are great for the brain; the problem is, we don't eat enough of them. Polyunsaturated fats include two important essential fatty acids that are critical for a well-functioning brain, but one is better than the other. They are omega-3 fatty acids and omega-6 fatty acids.

Omega-3

Omega-3 fatty acids are most frequently found in fatty, oily fish, and in some dark green leafy plants and vegetables.

In the body, omega-3 fatty acids from food are broken down into two other fatty acids, *eicosapentaenoic acid* (EPA) and *docosahexanenoic acid* (DHA). Healthy, well-functioning brains contain high amounts of DHA, which provides the perfect raw material for well-functioning cell membranes. Maintaining the optimal amount of DHA for the brain, however, can be a problem. Although the body has no trouble making enough EPA, many people are unable to produce adequate amounts of DHA on their own. Excess consumption of bad fats can interfere with the conversion of omega-3s to DHA. Low levels of DHA in adults are associated with decreased cognitive function, depression, moodiness, irritability, slow response time, and Alzheimer's disease.

> **AGELESS MIND FACT**
>
> The best source for omega-3 DHA is fish, especially halibut, sardines, and tuna.

Think of omega-3s as the smartest, happiest, and most energetic of all fats. When you lack omega-3s, your body will choose other fats instead, leaving the feeling slow and tired, with no energy left for thinking. Omega-3 fatty acids provide many benefits including improved mood, strengthened cognition, and disease prevention.

Sources of Omega-3

- Fatty fish - salmon, tuna, sardines, herring, and others
- Flaxseeds and flaxseed oil
- Walnuts
- oregano
- broccoli

Alternative Sources of Omega-3

- Krill – shrimp-like ocean creatures harvested for their omega-3 oil
- Algae –microalgae oil offers a viable source of Omega-3 DHA, but is often low in EPA

Healthy Benefits from the Sea

Omega-3 fatty acids are great for mental clarity, concentration, and focus. They play an essential role throughout life and are critical to maintaining an ageless mind. Omega-3 fatty acids:

1. Act as anti-inflammatories.
2. Critically support brain and nerve development.
3. Reduce the chance of stroke.
4. Support positive mood.
5. Lower blood pressure and cholesterol.
6. Assist with attention deficit disorder (ADD).
7. Reduce menstrual pain.
8. Reduce the risk of Alzheimer's Disease.

Omega-6

Omega-6 fatty acids are found in cooking oils, nuts, and most seeds and cereals. Vegetable oils (corn oil, peanut oil, sunflower oil, and margarine) are the primary sources of omega-6 fatty acids in the diet and, unfortunately, are not the best fats for the brain. Some forms of omega-6 can even promote free radical production and inflammation. On other hand, other forms of omega-6 such as ***gamma-linolenic acid*** (GLA) can be healthier and even act as a powerful anti-inflammatory. Good sources of GLA include avocados, walnuts, seeds, and borage oil, an oil made from the borage plant that is sold in capsules as a nutritional supplement.

Sources of Omega-6

- Vegetable oil (corn oil, peanut oil, sunflower oil)
- Soybean oil

Omega-6 fatty acids help regulate blood clotting, cell production, skin and hair growth, metabolism, the reproductive system, and inflammation. They can also help with rheumatoid arthritis, allergies, eczema, psoriasis, and rosacea. Sounds good, right? But these benefits come only when omega-6s are in the right ratio with omega-3s; too many omega-6s can create inflammation inside your body.

Finding the Balance Between Omega-3 and Omega-6

For optimum brain and body health, we do need a small amount of omega-6 fats in our diet to receive the benefits mentioned above. The problem is that you're likely already getting too many omega-6s through processed oils and food -food frequently purchased from grocery store shelves and fast-food restaurants.

The imbalance of high levels of omega-6 relative to omega-3 fats can contribute to brain health problems. The ratio of omega-6 fats ingested versus omega-3 fats in a typical American diet is 20 to 1, but the goal we should strive for is a ratio closer to 3 to 1.

Saturated Fats

Meat and dairy products are the major sources of saturated fat in the American diet. They are also the major source of protein in our diet. Protein is important for cell repair and maintenance, with adequate amounts required to keep the brain functioning at its peak. Getting the proper amount of protien, however, does not require one to fill-up on bad fat. In limited amounts, saturated fat is fine, but most of us eat about three times the amount we should every day.

Cutting Back on Saturated Fat

Try to find ways of cutting back on your daily amount of saturated fat. For example, not all cuts of beef are high in saturated fat. If you choose to eat beef, stick to the leanest cuts of beef. Game meats (venison, buffalo) are growing in popularity in the United States and are extremely lean. You don't have

> **HEALTHY BRAIN TIP**
>
> Extra virgin olive oil offers a healthy alternative in spreads, dressing, and some cooking.

to give up dairy, but use reduced-fat or no-fat dairy products and choose organic products if possible. Soy-based foods, such as tofu, can also provide low-saturated fat alternatives to meat.

Sources of Saturated Fat

- High-fat cuts of meat
- Chicken with the skin
- Whole-fat dairy products
- Egg yolks
- Butter
- Cheese
- Ice cream
- Palm and coconut oil
- Lard

Trans Fats

Trans fat is made by adding hydrogen to vegetable oil through a process called *hydrogenation*, which makes the oil less likely to spoil. The process creates the trans-fatty acids, a synthetic fat that is unlike any fat found in nature. Using trans fats in the manufacturing of foods helps foods stay fresh longer, have a longer shelf life, and become more stable at room temperature.

Also known as hydrogenated fats or partially hydrogenated fats, trans fats are often found in shortening, margarine, cookies, crackers, and snack foods. One reason America has become a nation of overweight people is that our consumption of essential fatty acids has declined by more than 80 percent while our consumption of trans fats has skyrocketed to more than 2,500%. If you want your brain to be healthy and happy, limit hydrogenated trans fats in your diet.

Besides greatly increasing your chance of gaining too much weight on foods that contain little to zero nutritional value, here's a short list of the damage trans fats can do to your brain:

Negative Effects of Trans Fats

- Alter the synthesis of neurotransmitters, such as dopamine. Increases LDL (bad) cholesterol and decreases HDL (good) cholesterol.
- Increase the amount of plaque in blood vessels and the possibility of blood clots forming, both of which put your heart and your brain at risk.
- Increase the amount of triglycerides in your system, which slows down the amount of oxygen going to your brain; the excess of which has been linked to depression.
- Disrupt the production of energy in the mitochondria (the energy factories) of brain cells.
- Force out healthier fats. Even if you eat plenty of good fat along with trans-fatty acids and take a fatty acid supplement, the trans-fats are the ones that get used in cell membrane production first.

Trans Fats and Nutritional Labels

Food manufacturers in the United States and many other countries list the trans fat content on nutrition labels. Trans fat used to be more common, but in recent years food manufacturers have used it less because of concerns over its health effects.

That does not mean, however, that you should not read the nutritional labels closely when it comes to identifying trans fat. In the United States, if a food contains less than 0.5 grams of trans fat per serving, the food label is allowed to read "0" grams trans fat. Though that's a small amount of trans fat, if you eat multiple servings of foods with less than 0.5 grams of trans fat, you could quickly exceed recommended limits.

3 Ways to Avoid Trans Fats

1. **Don't eat fried food.** This includes French fries, donuts, and most chips (corn, cheese, and potato). Baked chips may contain hydrogenated oils, so read the labels before eating these foods.

2. **Don't deep-fry food.** Any fat heated at a high temperature (with the oil bubbling hot) will result in trans-fatty acids. Instead, bake, sauté (with a low flame), steam, or grill.

3. **Read food labels.** Don't buy products that contain partially hydrogenated vegetable oil or shortening. Even if the label says it has 0 grams, food can be advertised as "trans fat free" if it has anything less than 0.5 grams per serving. The American Heart Association allots only 1% of your daily calories to trans fats – less than 2 grams a day. Don't assume that a so-called healthy food, such as whole-grain bread, does not contain hydrogenated oils. Trans-fatty acids pop up in the least likely places. Read the ingredients label to be sure.

Sources of Trans fats

- Commercially baked pastries like cookies, doughnuts, cakes, muffins, and pizza dough
- Packaged snack foods like chips, crackers and microwave popcorn
- Stick margarine
- Vegetable shortening
- Fried foods like french fries, fried chicken and nuggets, and breaded fish
- Candy bars
- Breakfast cereal and cereal bars
- Salad dressing

Fats and Your Ageless Mind

Fat is essential to brain structure and function, but when it comes to healthy brain nutrition, the type of fat we ingest is just as important as the amount. Eating too much of any kind of fat can lead to weight issues and part of being healthy means learning to balance the good fats with the bad.

Most of us have no problem getting enough of the bad fats – the greasy cheeseburger, french fries, and milkshake from the local fast food restaurant are easy to come by. It is the act of taking the time to eat healthier that is a challenge.

To protect our brains, we need to limit our intake of saturated fats – as well as say good-bye to dangerous trans fats - and instead choose the grilled wild salmon as an entrée and perhaps a handful of walnuts as a snack. These substitutions are rich in omega-3 fatty acids that protect the heart and brain. Numerous studies have shown that people who consume large amounts of anti-inflammatory omega-3 fatty acids have a lower risk of developing Alzheimer's disease. Now it is your turn to make those changes in your own diet and stock-up on those omega-3s for your ageless mind.

CHAPTER TWELVE

Vitamins & Supplements

" *To all my little Hulkamaniacs out there: say your prayers, take your vitamins, and you will never go wrong.* "

Hulk Hogan

VITAMINS & SUPPLEMENTS

Supplements are vitamins, minerals, amino acids (the building blocks of protein), herbs, essential fatty acids, and phytochemicals (extracts from plants) that work in synergy with food to recharge the brain and protect it against damage and inflammation. Supplements cannot replace a good diet, but they can compensate for nutrient deficiencies that are a result of a poor diet or drugs that deplete the body of vital nutrients.

Advantages for Brain Health

Can the appropriate use of vitamins and supplements make you healthier? According to Michael F. Roizen, MD, "The right nutrients in the proper amounts help protect your mind and body from needless aging." For many years, the American Medical Association's official position was that vitamin supplementation was unnecessary for healthy adults. They've since changed their stance and now advocate daily multivitamins to promote general health and prevent a range of chronic ailments. A report in the New England Journal of Medicine stated, "The evidence suggests that people who take vitamins and supplements are healthier." In a study published in the medical journal *The Lancet*, ninety students were assigned to one of three groups: one received a multivitamin and mineral supplement; the second received an identical-looking placebo; and the third received nothing. After seven months, the IQ of those taking the supplements had increased by nine points.

Supplementing Your Diet

Unfortunately, modern food-processing techniques have depleted the food supply of many vital nutrients (such as B vitamins, vitamins C and E, and the essential fatty acids) that are critical for health. The storage and shipping of food, especially fruits and vegetables, can also sap it of its nutrients. If you don't supplement your diet of these missing nutrients, it is easy to fall short of them and suffer serious health consequences. Moreover, the body's production of key antioxidants (such as Co-Q10 and alpha lipoic acid) slows down with age, which leaves us more vulnerable to free radical attack. In addition, many commonly used over-the-counter and prescription medicines also deplete the body of important vitamins. Taking supplements can fill the nutritional gap and help maintain optimal mental and physical health.

Adding Vitamins to Your Diet

Vitamin B

Although vitamin B12 is abundant in fish, chicken, eggs, and many meats, not all adults absorb adequate amounts from their diet, so B vitamins are usually included in multivitamin supplements. Folate, or folic acid (an antioxidant B vitamin), is recommended during pregnancy to prevent fetal neural defects. It may also protect older adults from developing strokes and heart disease.

These two B vitamins as well as B6 are involved in the breakdown of *homocysteine*, one of the amino acid building blocks of protein in the body. Scientists recently found that high levels of homocysteine in the blood increase the risk of Alzheimer's disease. Moreover, lower blood levels of these B vitamins and higher blood levels of homocysteine are associated with cognitive decline.

Oxford University investigators gave either daily B vitamins (folic acid, B12, and B6) or a placebo to study volunteers with mild cognitive impairment. After two years, those receiving the B vitamins had significantly less cognitive decline, and their MRI scans showed less brain shrinkage than the others' scans. The greatest response to the B vitamins was seen in volunteers with the highest homocysteine levels at the beginning of the study.

B vitamins are critical to the synthesis of DNA and protect brain health by maintaining neural cell integrity. A recent study found that vitamin B12 may help the body control inflammation. Although some people take very high doses of B vitamins, megadoses of these vitamins (as compared to the Recommended Daily Allowance), have not consistently been found to provide additional benefits. As always, consult your doctor when starting any new vitamin or supplement.

Vitamin C

Recent studies, such as the one published in *Seminars in Prevention and Alternative Medicine*, highlight the many benefits of vitamin C. The lead author, Mark Moyad of the University of Michigan, comments, "The more we study vitamin C, the better our understanding of how diverse it is in protecting our health." Moyad cites benefits including better visual acuity, strengthened immune function, and enhanced resistance to cancer and cardiovascular disease. Although controversy continues regarding the ideal dosage, the good news is that vitamin C is relatively safe. It may not be the cure for the common cold, but vitamin C has many benefits.

Vitamin D

Even though sunlight and milk products provide healthy doses of vitamin D, many people are deficient in this vitamin because they spend much of their time indoors and use sunblock outdoors. Vitamin D not only keeps bones strong and prevents fractures, it also protects brain health. Low levels of vitamin D are associated with extensive cognitive decline. In a study of more than 5,000 older women, those taking the recommended weekly amount of at least 35 micrograms of a vitamin D supplement had better cognitive ability than those who did not.

Vitamin D is essential for regulating the absorption of calcium and plays a significant role in bone health. Studies suggest that it may provide protection from osteoporosis, high blood pressure, a range of autoimmune conditions, and dementia.

Vitamin E

In the late 1990's, Dr. Mary Sanyo and her collaborators reported that Alzheimer's patients who took 2,000 units of the antioxidant vitamin E had slower declines in everyday function compared with those taking a placebo. Following that report, Alzheimer's experts started recommending high doses of vitamin E supplements for their patients. In 2005, however, Dr. Edgar Miller and colleagues reported that patients taking megadoses of vitamin E increased their risk of heart attacks and even death. Today, few doctors advocate the use of over 400 daily units of vitamin E for brain protection.

Multi-Vitamins

If taking a multi-vitamin, make sure it contains at least 400 mcg of folic acid and 500 mg of vitamin C. Folic acid reduces homocysteine, a known risk factor for heart disease and strokes. Dr. Snowdon discovered that the greatest brain damage was associated with the lowest blood levels of folic acid and the least brain damage with the highest levels. 400 – 1,000 mcg is the suggested dosage and is recommended to be taken with vitamin B12.

Supplement Your Prescription

Many prescription drugs deplete the vitamins and minerals you need to overcome the health condition for which the drugs were prescribed. This medical "catch-22" affects patients who take many commonly prescribed pharmaceuticals for conditions such as elevated blood pressure, high cholesterol, chronic heartburn ("GERD"), arthritis, diabetes, and depression. In her book, Supplement Your Prescription, Dr. Hyla Cass discusses the nutrient depletion you can expect from commonly prescribed drugs and suggests how to correct them. As she explains, "The prescription drugs you are taking can actually make your condition worse!" Cass further states, "The truth is, most doctors have very little knowledge about nutrition and how it affects your overall health and well-being. As a result, your doctor is unlikely to tell you how to supplement your prescription."

> **AGELESS MIND FACT**
>
> Many doctors either do not take into consideration or understand the effects of medications on nutrition.

6 Supplements to Consider

It seems that every day a new wonder-supplement promises to solve all of our problems. While such a supplement likely doesn't exist, here are some of the best-researched options that may protect your brain and help you stay mentally strong.

CoEnzyme Q10 (CoQ10)

Coenzyme Q10 (CoQ10) is a substance found naturally in the body that helps convert food into energy. CoQ10 is found in almost every cell in the body and is a powerful antioxidant.

AGELESS MIND FACT

CoQ10 can cause rare but dangerous side-effects for those taking blood pressure medication or chemotherapy. Talk to your doctor first.

Antioxidants fight damaging effects of free radicals throughout the body. Scientists believe free radicals contribute to the aging process, as well as a number of health problems, including heart disease and cancer. Antioxidants, such as CoQ10, can neutralize free radicals and may reduce or even help prevent some of the damage they cause.

Primary dietary sources of CoQ10 include oily fish (such as salmon and tuna), organ meats (such as liver), and whole grains. Most people get enough CoQ10 through a balanced diet, but supplements may help people with particular health conditions.

Alpha Lipoic Acid

Alpha-lipoic acid is another antioxidant that is made by the body and is found in every cell. Other names for it include lipoic acid, thioctic acid, and ALA. It is needed by the body to produce the energy for our body's normal functions, converting glucose (blood sugar) into energy.

While other antioxidants work only in water (such as vitamin C) or fatty tissues (such as vitamin E), alpha-lipoic acid is both fat and water-soluble. That means it can work throughout the body. Antioxidants in the body are used up as they attack free radicals, but evidence suggests alpha-lipoic acid may help regenerate these other antioxidants and make them active again.

Because alpha-lipoic acid can pass easily into the brain, it may help protect the brain and nerve tissue. Researchers are still deciding if it as a potential treatment for stroke and other brain problems involving free radical damage, such as dementia, but the evidence is far from conclusive.

Alpha lipoic acid can be found in very small amounts in foods such as spinach, broccoli, peas, Brussel sprouts, rice bran, and organ meats. Alpha lipoic acid supplements are also vailable in capsule form. For maximum absorption, the supplements should be taken on an empty stomach.

Ginkgo Biloba

Ginkgo biloba, widely touted as a "brain herb," is often associated with memory enhancement. Harvested from the leaves of one of the oldest living tree species, this medicinal herb has been the focus of many scientific tests attempting to verify its purported health benefits. While some studies have found it to be beneficial in the improvement of memory, other study results have demonstrated little or no effect on memory at all.

The use of medicinal herbs is a time-honored approach to strengthening the body and treating disease. Herbs, however, contain components that can trigger side effects and interact with other herbs, supplements, or medications. For these reasons, herbs should be taken with care, under the supervision of a health care provider qualified in the field of botanical medicine.

Ginkgo usually has few side effects. In a few cases, upset stomach, headaches, skin reactions, and dizziness were reported. It is important to note that ginko, like aspirin, is a natural blood thinner. You should ask your doctor before taking ginkgo if you also take blood-thinning drugs.

Turmeric/Curcumin

The earliest known mention of a curry – a spicy sauce with meat and bread – is etched onto tablets found in Babylon dating back to around 1700BC. While not everyone loves this historic dish or Indian food in general, its powerful benefits can be found in supplement form. Curcumin, the active ingredient in turmeric (and curry powder), is a both a powerful antioxidant and anti-inflammatory.

It is this same curcumin which is also believed to help prevent Alzheimer's disease. Studies by the University of California at Los Angeles (UCLA) have shown that when curcumin is given to aging mice, the plaques that are found in the brain that lead to Alzheimer's are blocked. Although research so far has only been carried out on mice, the benefits for humans could potentially be groundbreaking.

It has been reported in the *Medical News* (December 2004) that the occurrence of Alzheimer's in adults in India aged between 70-79 years was 4.4 times less than the same age group in the United States. With diet being the main difference between the two groups, the results certainly look promising.

There are, however, a few precautions for taking turmeric or curcumin. Don't use turmeric if you have gallstones or bile duct dysfunction. Pregnant women shouldn't use it without their doctors' approval. In rare cases, extended use can cause stomach upset or heartburn. Some evidence also suggests that curcumin can interfere with a chemotherapy agent used to treat breast cancer, so if you're being treated for this disease, be sure to discuss the advisability of taking curcumin with your physician.

Phosphatidylserine (PS)

Phosphatidylserine (PS) is a nutrient we get from several foods, including tuna, herring, eel, and soy products. It serves as an important structural component of cell membranes throughout the body. Controlled studies using phosphatidylserine supplements have demonstrated its cognitive benefits in people with mild age-related memory complaints, as well as people suffering from dementia.

A recent double-blind study from Sourasky Medical Center, in Tel Aviv, Israel, used a combination of phosphatidylserine (300 milligrams daily) with the omega-3 fatty acid DHA in older adults with age-related complaints. After four months of treatment, the investigators found significant improvements in verbal memory abilities in the supplement group compared to a group taking a placebo.

In another study, Japanese investigators used soybean-derived phosphatidylserine and found that after six months of treatment, people with mild cognitive impairment (aged 50 to 69 years) had better memory performance compared to a group taking a placebo. Laboratory studies of phosphatidylserine suggest that it may protect brain health and improve cognitive performance by stabilizing brain cell membranes and improving the function of neural transmitters that influence memory ability.

Phosphatidylserine is often used to help age-related decline in mental function, attention deficit-hyperactivity disorder (ADHD), depression, preventing exercise-induced stress, and improving athletic performance. The body can make phosphatidylserine, but gets most of what it needs from foods. Supplements made from cabbage or soy are available in capsule form.

Dococahexaenoic Acid (DHA) / Omega-3

Daily fish oil is a universally popular supplement for protecting the well-being of the brain. Pharmaceutical-grade fish oil, free from mercury and other toxins, provides the omega-3 fatty acids that are essential for your health. Fish oil helps to strengthen the immune system, improves your circulation, and counters inflammation in a way that can provide relief for arthritis and joint pain. Rich in DMAE, a nutrient that supports the important memory neurotransmitter acetylcholine, as well as in the essential fatty acids eicosapentaenoic acid (EPA) and docosahexaenoic acid (DHA), fish oil has demonstrated benefits in preventing depression, stabilizing mood, and promoting alertness.

In a study at Tufts University, DHA was identified as the component in fish oil that protects brains from dementia and Alzheimer's disease. In a large sample of older Americans, those with the highest blood levels of DHA were about half as apt to develop dementia and 39% were as apt to develop Alzheimer's as those with lower blood levels of DHA over a nine-year period. The top 25% of those with the highest blood DHA got about 180 mg DHA a day, or three servings of fish a week, researchers said. In this study, the other major fatty acid in fish oil, EPA, had no effect.

> **HEALTHY BRAIN TIP**
>
> Tired of getting nasty "fish burps" from your omega-3 supplements? Putting fish oil pills in the freezer will help put an end to the burps.

Fish oil supplements come in both liquid and pill form, sometimes flavored with lemon or berries to mask the taste. Shop carefully for your fish oil pills. You want to purchase a bottle of fish oil that contains 30% of the recommended daily amount (RDA) of DHA. If it does, the bottle will read that each pill contains 180 milligrams of EPA and 120 milligrams of DHA.

Vitamins & Supplement Strategies

Take all supplements with meals, as most supplements are best absorbed when taken with food. When taking them twice a day, the first dose could be at breakfast and the second dose with lunch or dinner. Unless advised by your doctor, it is best to avoid taking them before bed. Consuming vitamins just before bed, (speaking from personal experience), can result in a painful erosion of soft tissue similar to GERD symptoms as the undigested acids eat away at your gastric lining.

Supplements and the Food and Drug Administration

When it comes to purchasing vitamins and supplements, many people take product safety and effectiveness for granted. Before you send your money away for that next miracle cure, there are a few things you should know.

1. Supplements are not regulated in the same way by the FDA and do not require the scrutiny and testing that over-the-counter and prescription medicines receive. While they may be taken for health benefits, specific claims as to their effectiveness often do not have the supporting evidence required to legally advertise such health claims in the U.S.

2. Under the Dietary Supplement Health and Education Act of 1994 (DSHEA), the dietary supplement manufacturer itself is responsible for ensuring that a supplement or ingredient it produces is safe before it is marketed. Unlike drug products that must be proven safe and effective before they arrive into the marketplace, there are no provisions in the law for the FDA to "approve" dietary supplements for safety or effectiveness before they reach the consumer.

3. Recent tests by a public safety group found that of 83 supplement products randomly tested, more than half either contained less than the active ingredient advertised, included the wrong ingredient, or in some cases, lacked the active ingredient entirely.

Storage

Most supplements should be stored in a cool, dry place away from direct light or heat. Some manufacturers may tell you to refrigerate a product after it is open, so be sure to read the label carefully.

Dosage

The right combination of timing and dosage of supplements will depend on your age, gender, weight, and health. Also, be sure to keep in mind that the effectiveness of supplements is a function of the way that they are absorbed by your system. That's one reason why higher quality vitamins and minerals are often worth the investment. Consult a qualified healthcare provider with special expertise in nutrition before taking supplements. A knowledgeable practitioner can help you discover the optimal combination that your body can absorb and utilize.

Choosing a Quality Product

With hundreds of brands of supplements on the market, it can be a daunting task to choose the right one. Safety should always come first. Look for products that come in tamper-proof packages with an expiration date on the label. Try to find a product that has a quality-control number on the package; that way, if there is any problem, the manufacturer can quickly recall a tainted product. If you have a choice, select manufacturers that offer a guaranteed potency product, which means the supplement contains the right amount of the active ingredient. In particular, studies of many herbal products have shown that many contain little, if any, active ingredient. Look for products that are pharmaceutical grade, which are of the highest quality and free of impurities.

Vitamins, Supplements, and Your Ageless Mind

As we grow older we, want to make the right decisions for our health and nutrition. No vitamin supplement can ever replace a healthy diet, which provides vitamins, minerals, and a host of other naturally occurring nutrients necessary for your brain and body. With medicines depleting us of nutrients and with often poor nutritional habits to start with, however, many people are turning towards supplements. If you are considering starting a vitamin or supplement, do your homework to see if it is right for you. Talk with your doctor and discuss your personal needs and what other medicines you are taking to prevent interactions (such as blood thinners and cancer treatments).

Keep in mind that just because something is "natural" doesn't mean that it's necessarily good for you. We can list many things, such as poison ivy and nightshade, that are both natural and harmful. For some people, like those taking blood thinners, this list could even include gingko biloba. The bottom line is to treat any medicinal supplement with respect and to learn the potential side effects and drug interactions before taking.

As with any health decision, proper research and common sense will go a long way in making the best choices for your ageless mind.

Brain Recipes

*Let food be thy medicine and
medicine be thy food.*

Hippocrates

HEALTHY BRAIN RECIPES

What you eat not only affects your waistline - it also affects your brain. According to current studies, diet may rank among the top factors that will determine your risk of getting Alzheimer's disease. Fortunately, diet may also be one of the easiest things to modify to help reduce your risk.

The connection between diet and dementia is a growing area of research, with an already large body of scientific evidence from population and animal-based studies. What it shows is that when it comes to Alzheimer's, what you eat matters. By adopting simple nutritional strategies, not only can you protect your long term brain function; you may also substantially reduce your risk of heart disease and ultimately improve your health overall.

Five Stages of a Healthy Diet

The following pages will provide a starting point for your dietary journey. Twenty-five brain-boosting recipes have been divided into the following categories:

- Breakfast
- Lunch
- Soups & Salads
- Entrées
- Desserts

Each category will also feature selected key ingredients and their healthy benefits. Feel free to modify the recipes in this chapter as you wish. The end goal is to provide you with tools you will use to help keep your brain healthy and strong.

BREAKFAST

Have you heard that breakfast is the most important meal of the day? Well, it's true. After fasting overnight, breakfast is essential to stimulate your metabolism and provide the energy your body requires until lunch. It is also essential for your ageless mind.

According to neuroscientist Valerie Gremillion, PhD, "Breakfast establishes the core support for your brain function throughout the day and creates the conditions for enhancing mood, attitude, and motivation." You can optimize your brain functioning and overall health by starting your day with fresh fruits, whole grains, and proteins.

Featured Ingredients

Bananas

Bananas are rich in vitamin B6 and are a good source of fiber, vitamin C, magnesium, and potassium. Lack of B6 in a diet can cause weakness, irritability and insomnia. The potassium found in bananas helps to regulate blood pressure and may reduce the risk of hypertension and stroke. Potassium also helps muscles contract while exercising.

Spinach

Leafy green spinach is loaded with beneficial nutrients to protect the body from disease, including 13 flavonoids that help to fight cancer, protect against age related memory loss, and prevent heart disease. The magnesium in spinach also helps to lower high blood pressure and protect against heart disease, while vitamins C and A help prevent oxidation.

Oats

Oatmeal, oat bran, and whole oat products are some of the best sources of soluble fiber, which help reduce total cholesterol along with LDL or "bad" cholesterol. In addition to reducing the risk of heart disease, oat fiber can help control blood sugar, too. That's why it's often added to breakfast cereals, muffins, and other foods.

Banana Bran Muffins

INGREDIENTS

- 2 large eggs
- 2/3 cup packed light brown sugar
- 1 cup mashed ripe bananas, (2 medium)
- 1 cup buttermilk, (can be powdered)
- 1 cup unprocessed wheat bran, (miller's bran)
- 1/4 cup canola oil
- 1 teaspoon vanilla extract
- 1 cup whole-wheat flour
- 3/4 cup all-purpose flour
- 1-1/2 teaspoons baking powder
- 1/2 teaspoon baking soda
- 1/2 teaspoon ground cinnamon
- 1/4 teaspoon salt
- 1/2 cup chocolate chips (optional)
- 1/3 cup chopped walnuts (optional)

PREPARATION

- Preheat oven to 400°F. Coat 12 muffin cups with cooking spray.
- Whisk eggs and brown sugar in a medium bowl until smooth. Whisk in bananas, buttermilk, wheat bran, oil and vanilla.
- Whisk whole-wheat flour, all-purpose flour, baking powder, baking soda, cinnamon, and salt in a large bowl. Make a well in the dry ingredients; add the wet ingredients and stir with a rubber spatula until just combined. Stir in chocolate chips, if using. Scoop the batter into the prepared muffin cups (they'll be quite full). Sprinkle with walnuts, if using.
- Bake the muffins until the tops are golden brown and spring back when touched lightly, 15 to 25 minutes. Let cool in the pan for 5 minutes. Loosen edges and turn muffins out onto a wire rack to cool slightly before serving.

Makes 1 dozen

Spinach Scramble

INGREDIENTS

- 6 eggs
- 1/2 cup milk
- 1 teaspoon salt
- 1 teaspoon pepper
- 2 cups fresh spinach leaves, cleaned and chopped
- 1 tablespoon + 2 teaspoons olive oil, divided
- 4-5 green onions, cleaned and chopped finely (white part and half of green part)

PREPARATION

- Whisk eggs (or just egg whites), milk, salt and pepper in a bowl until well combined.
- Heat 1 tablespoon oil in a non-stick sauté pan over medium-high heat.
- Add spinach and cook about 2–3 minutes, tossing to wilt.
- Remove spinach from pan and set aside.
- Turn heat down to medium. In the same pan, add remaining 2 teaspoons oil and heat. Add eggs and cook, scraping bottom and sides and folding them over continuously, until cooked through.
- Turn off heat and stir in spinach and green onions. Serve with whole grain toast.

Serves 4

Blueberry Granola Bars

INGREDIENTS

- 1/2 cup honey
- 1/4 cup packed brown sugar
- 3 tablespoons canola oil
- 1-1/2 teaspoons ground cinnamon
- 1-1/2 cups quick-cooking oats
- 2 cups fresh blueberries

PREPARATION

- Preheat oven to 350°F.
- Lightly grease a 9x9 inch square baking pan.
- In a medium-sized saucepan combine honey, brown sugar, oil, and cinnamon and bring to a boil. Continue boiling for 2 minutes without stirring.
- In a large mixing bowl, combine oats and blueberries. Stir in honey mixture until thoroughly blended.
- Spread into the prepared baking pan, gently pressing mixture flat. Bake until lightly browned, about 40 minutes.
- Cool completely in a pan on a wire rack. Cut into 1-1/2 by 3 inch bars.

Makes 6

Banana-Berry Smoothie

INGREDIENTS

- 1 ripe banana, sliced
- 1/2 cup raspberries
- 1/4 cup blueberries
- 1-1/2 teaspoons honey
- 1/8 teaspoon ground cinnamon
- 1/2 cup unsweetened apple juice
- 1/2 cup ice

PREPARATION

- Place ingredients in the order listed in a blender.
- Pulse twice to chop the fruit, stir well, then blend until smooth.
- Serve immediately.

Makes 2 cups

Multi-Grain Waffles

INGREDIENTS

- 2 cups buttermilk
- 1/2 cup old-fashioned rolled oats
- 2/3 cup whole-wheat flour
- 2/3 cup all-purpose flour
- 1/4 cup toasted wheat germ (or cornmeal)
- 1-1/2 teaspoons baking powder
- 1/2 teaspoon baking soda
- 1/4 teaspoon salt
- 1 teaspoon ground cinnamon
- 2 large eggs, lightly beaten
- 1/4 cup packed brown sugar
- 1 tablespoon canola oil
- 2 teaspoons vanilla extract

PREPARATION

- Mix buttermilk and oats in a medium bowl; let stand for 15 minutes.
- Whisk whole-wheat flour, all-purpose flour, wheat germ (or cornmeal), baking powder, baking soda, salt, and cinnamon in a large bowl.
- Stir eggs, sugar, oil and vanilla into the oat mixture. Add the wet ingredients to the dry ingredients; mix with a rubber spatula just until moistened.
- Coat a waffle iron with cooking spray and preheat. Spoon in enough batter to cover three-fourths of the surface (about 2/3 cup for an 8x8 inch waffle iron). Cook until waffles are crisp and golden brown, 4 to 5 minutes. (Freeze any uneaten waffles for later.)

Makes 12-16

LUNCH

Food gives us energy and eating a nutrient-packed lunch gives us the power we need for the second half of the day. We've all had the experience of missing lunch and feeling hungry (and cranky) by the end of the day. This is often followed by overeating or the temptation to hit the drive-thru later on. Lunch may be the second most important meal of the day, but it doesn't have to be difficult.

The key to healthy lunches lies in preparation. Stock up on nutritious ingredients and, if busy, prepare elements of your lunch the day before. You will find that even a "gourmet chicken sandwich" can be quick and easy if some of the measuring is already done.

Featured Ingredients

Chicken

If there is one word that describes chicken, it is versatility. Roasted, broiled, grilled or poached, and combined with a wide range of herbs and spices, chicken makes a flavorful and nutritious meal. Chicken is a very good source of protein, providing 67.6% of the daily value for protein in 4 ounces. To cut calories, don't eat the skin, and always be sure to cook to an internal temperature of 165°F to kill bacteria.

Tuna

At nearly 40 grams of protein per can, tuna fish has all the essentials to be the perfect brain-building food. Tuna fish is low in fat, high in protein, and provides an essential form of omega-3 fatty acids. Besides helping to lower cholesterol levels, tuna has also been shown to fight heart disease and is associated with the prevention of some forms of cancer.

Black Beans

Black beans are a good source of cholesterol-lowering fiber, as are most other legumes. Their high fiber content also prevents blood sugar levels from rising too rapidly after a meal, making these beans an especially good choice for individuals with diabetes, insulin resistance, or hypoglycemia. When combined with whole grains such as brown rice, black beans provide a low fat, high-quality protein.

Smoked Salmon Melts

INGREDIENTS

- 6 oz. smoked salmon filet (not lox)
- 2 tablespoons mayonnaise
- 1 teaspoon grainy or Dijon mustard
- 1/2 teaspoon lemon juice
- 1 large or 2 small shallots, minced
- Pinch each of salt and pepper
- 2 thin slices Havarti, Swiss, or Jack cheese
- 4 slices of soft sandwich bread
- butter or olive oil for grilling

PREPARATION

- Use a fork to flake the salmon into small pieces in a bowl. Add mayonnaise, mustard, lemon, shallots, and salt and pepper, and mix well.
- Spread half of the salmon mixture onto one piece of bread and half onto another. Top each with a slice of cheese and the remaining bread slices.
- Spread a little butter or brush olive oil on the outsides of the bread. Cook in a sauté pan over medium low heat to toast the bread on both sides, warm the salmon, and melt the cheese a bit. Serve immediately.

Serves 2

Gourmet Chicken Sandwich

INGREDIENTS

- 4 skinless, boneless chicken breast halves - pounded to 1/4 inch thickness
- Ground black pepper to taste
- 1 tablespoon olive oil
- 1 teaspoon minced garlic
- 2 tablespoons mayonnaise
- 2 teaspoons Dijon mustard
- 1 teaspoon chopped fresh rosemary
- 8 slices garlic and rosemary focaccia bread

PREPARATION

- Sprinkle pepper on one side of each chicken cutlet. Heat oil in a large skillet; brown garlic in oil, then add chicken, pepper-side-down. Sauté chicken until cooked through and juices run clear, about 12 to 15 minutes.
- In a small bowl combine the mayonnaise, mustard, and rosemary. Mix together and spread mixture on 4 slices of focaccia bread. Place 1 chicken cutlet on each of these slices, then top each with another bread slice.

Serves 4

Mediterranean Tuna Sandwich

INGREDIENTS

- 1 red onion, sliced very thinly
- 1 tomato, chopped
- 2 cans albacore tuna in water, drained
- 2 tablespoons capers
- 1 cup spinach leaves, chopped
- 2 cloves garlic, sliced lengthwise
- 1/4 cup extra virgin olive oil
- 1/2 cup red wine vinegar
- 1 teaspoon salt
- 1/2 teaspoon cracked black pepper
- 8 slices fresh whole grain bread

PREPARATION

- Preheat oven to 350°F.
- Whisk oil and vinegar in a bowl together with salt and pepper, and marinate onion slices and tomatoes in it for about 10 minutes. Meanwhile, rub cut side of garlic onto bread and toast bread slices. Set aside.
- Remove tomatoes and onions from marinade and put into a larger bowl, reserving marinade.
- Combine tuna, capers, and spinach with tomatoes and onions.
- Divide tuna mixture among 4 slices of bread. Drizzle with a bit of the reserved marinade and top with remaining bread slices.

Serves 4

Chicken Salad with Olive Vinaigrette

INGREDIENTS

- 1 cup uncooked Israeli couscous
- 1/4 cup chopped pitted kalamata olives
- 2 tablespoons chopped, fresh flat-leaf parsley
- 1 tablespoon chopped capers
- 2 tablespoons extra-virgin olive oil
- 1 tablespoon fresh lemon juice
- 1/4 teaspoon salt
- 1/4 teaspoon freshly ground black pepper
- 1 garlic clove, minced
- 2 (7-ounce) packages 98% fat-free chicken breast in water

PREPARATION

- Cook couscous according to package directions, omitting salt and fat. Drain and rinse with cold water.
- Combine olives and next 7 ingredients (olives through garlic) in a large bowl, stirring with a whisk. Add couscous to olive mixture; toss gently to coat. Stir in chicken just before serving.

Serves 4

Black Bean Burritos

INGREDIENTS
- 2 (10-inch) flour tortillas
- 2 tablespoons vegetable oil
- 1 small onion, chopped
- 1/2 red bell pepper, chopped
- 1 teaspoon minced garlic
- 1 (15 oz.) can black beans, rinsed and drained
- 1 teaspoon minced jalapeno peppers
- 3 ounces cream cheese
- 1/2 teaspoon salt
- 2 tablespoons chopped, fresh cilantro

PREPARATION
- Wrap tortillas in foil and place in oven heated to 350°F. Bake for 15 minutes or until heated through.
- Heat oil in a 10-inch skillet over medium heat. Place onion, bell pepper, garlic and jalapenos in skillet, cook for 2 minutes stirring occasionally. Pour beans into skillet; cook 3 minutes stirring.
- Cut cream cheese into cubes and add to skillet with salt. Cook for 2 minutes stirring occasionally. Stir cilantro into mixture.
- Spoon mixture evenly down center of warmed tortilla and roll tortillas up. Serve immediately.

Makes 2

SOUPS & SALADS

Soups and salads are the all-purpose tool in the dietary arsenal. With a handful of healthy ingredients, you can put them together in a snap. You can serve them warm or cold, and they offer a variety of benefits, including reducing caloric consumption, if your aim is weight maintenance or weight loss.

By adding lean protein to a vegetable-rich base, soup or salad can become a meal on its own. Choosing the right ingredients not only increases the nutritional value of a soup or salad, but provides the makings for endless variations.

Featured Ingredients

Ginger
Besides adding a distinctive flavoring to dishes ranging from soup to Asian stir fries, ginger is a potent anti-inflammatory, helping to reduce inflammation in the body. Ginger has also been widely recognized to have the ability to calm an upset stomach and ease stomach cramping, as well as provide possible relief for nausea and other digestive problems.

Olive Oil
Olive oil's high content of monounsaturated fatty acids protects against heart disease by controlling LDL cholesterol levels while raising HDL or "good" cholesterol levels. In fact, olive oil has the highest amount of monounsaturated fatty acids of all naturally produced oils. The protective function of olive oil may have a beneficial effect on ulcers. Other research suggests that some compounds in olive oil may help prevent colon cancer.

Quinoa
Quinoa (pronounced KEEN-wah) is an excellent protein source, containing all essential amino acids while providing twice the amount of protein found in other cereal grains. Despite it's small size, quinoa is packed with beneficial minerals, including copper, iron, manganese, magnesium, potassium, as well as B-complex vitamins. Quinoa is also a good source of fiber with 5 grams per half-cup serving.

Carrot Ginger Soup

INGREDIENTS

- 1 tablespoon olive oil
- 1 medium onion, chopped coarsely
- 1 tablespoon curry powder
- 1 tablespoon fresh ginger, chopped
- 1-1/2 pounds carrots, peeled and chopped into 2 inch sections
- 1 teaspoon salt
- 6 cups chicken or vegetable broth
- 1/4 cup milk or cream

PREPARATION

- Heat oil in soup pot over medium high heat.
- Add onion and sauté until soft, about 4–5 minutes.
- Add curry powder and ginger and sauté about one minute.
- Add carrots and salt and cook, stirring for about 5 minutes.
- Add broth and bring to a boil. Cover and simmer on low until carrots are very soft.
- Remove from heat and purée using an immersion blender, or in batches in a regular blender.
- Put puréed soup into a bowl and stir in milk or cream. Serve immediately.

Serves 4

Sautéed Mushroom Salad

INGREDIENTS

* 2 tablespoons extra-virgin olive oil, divided
* 1 small onion, halved and sliced
* 1 pound white or cremini mushrooms, quartered
* 2 cloves garlic, minced
* 1-1/2 teaspoons chopped fresh thyme, or 1/2 teaspoon dried
* 3 tablespoons dry sherry
* 2 tablespoons lemon juice
* 1/4 teaspoon salt
* 1/4 teaspoon freshly ground pepper
* 8 cups bitter salad greens, such as frisee, arugula, or baby dandelion greens
* 2 tablespoons grated Parmesan cheese

PREPARATION

* Heat 1 tablespoon oil in a large nonstick skillet over medium heat. Add onion and cook until softened, about 3 minutes. Add mushrooms and cook, stirring until they release their juices, for 10 to 12 minutes.
* Add garlic and thyme and stir until fragrant, about 30 seconds. Add sherry and cook until mostly evaporated, about 3 minutes. Stir in the remaining 1 tablespoon oil, lemon juice, salt and pepper, and continue cooking for 1 minute more. Pour over greens in a large bowl and toss to coat. Sprinkle with Parmesan cheese.

Serves 4-6

Spinach & Feta Quinoa Salad

INGREDIENTS

- 1 tablespoon olive oil
- 1 small onion, chopped finely
- 2 cloves garlic, chopped finely
- 1 bunch spinach, roughly chopped
- 1 cup quinoa
- 2 cups vegetable broth (can substitute chicken broth or water)
- 1/4 cup parsley, chopped
- 1/4 cup dill, chopped
- 1/4 cup crumbled feta cheese
- Juice and zest of 1 lemon
- Salt and pepper

PREPARATION

- Heat olive oil in a large sauté pan over medium high heat. Add the onion and sauté until translucent, about 5-7 minutes.
- Add the garlic and sauté until fragrant, about a minute. Add the spinach and cook until it wilts, about 2-4 minutes.
- Add quinoa, broth, parsley, and dill and season with salt and pepper to taste. Bring to a boil. Reduce heat to low, cover, and simmer until the quinoa is tender, about 20 minutes.
- Remove from heat. Add lemon juice and zest, and mix in the feta. Serve immediately.

Serves 4

Southwestern Three-Bean & Barley Soup

INGREDIENTS

- 1 tablespoon extra-virgin olive oil
- 1 large onion, diced
- 1 large stalk celery, diced
- 1 large carrot, diced
- 9 cups water
- 4 cups (32-ounce carton) chicken broth or vegetable broth
- 1/2 cup pearl barley
- 1/3 cup dried black beans
- 1/3 cup dried great northern beans
- 1/3 cup dried kidney beans
- 1 tablespoon chili powder
- 1 teaspoon ground cumin
- 1/2 teaspoon dried oregano
- 3/4 teaspoon salt

PREPARATION

- Heat oil in a Dutch oven over medium heat. Add onion, celery, and carrot and cook, stirring occasionally, until softened, about 5 minutes.
- Add water, broth, barley, black beans, great northern beans, kidney beans, chili powder, cumin, and oregano. Bring to a lively simmer over high heat.
- Reduce heat to maintain a simmer and cook, stirring occasionally, until the beans are tender, 1-3/4 to 2-1/2 hours (adding more water, 1/2 cup at a time, if necessary or desired). Season with salt.

Serves 6

Toasted Pita & Bean Salad

INGREDIENTS

- 2 (6-inch) whole-wheat pita breads, cut or torn into bite-size pieces
- 2 cloves garlic, peeled
- 1/8 teaspoon salt
- 2 tablespoons fresh lemon juice
- 2 tablespoons ground toasted cumin seeds
- 3 tablespoons extra-virgin olive oil
- Freshly ground pepper to taste
- 2 cups cooked pinto beans, well drained and slightly warmed
- 1 cup diced plum tomatoes or 1/2 pint cherry tomatoes, quartered
- 1/2 cucumber, peeled and diced
- 1 cup sliced romaine lettuce
- 1 cup crumbled feta cheese
- 3 tablespoons chopped fresh parsley

PREPARATION

- Preheat oven to 400°F.
- Spread pita pieces out on a large baking sheet. Bake until crisp and beginning to brown, 5 to 7 minutes. Let cool on the pan.
- Mash garlic and salt with the back of a chef's knife to form a paste. Transfer to a bowl, add lemon juice and ground cumin and whisk to blend. Add oil in a slow, steady stream, whisking continually. Season with pepper.
- Place beans, tomatoes, and cucumber in a serving bowl. Add the toasted pita, lettuce, feta, parsley, and the dressing; toss to mix. Season with more pepper. Serve immediately.

Serves 4

ENTRÉES

When it comes to entrées, size matters. As Americans, we are used to over-sized portions, which lead us to overeat. If serving meat, stick to three ounces and fill the rest of your plate with vegetables and a starch.

Remember, it is possible to cook the nutrients out of vegetables. Lightly searing or steaming vegetables is a great way to ensure they don't lose their nutritional value. For additional flavor, balsamic vinaigrette, lemon juice, and black pepper are all great seasoning choices when added to side dishes.

Featured Ingredients

Salmon

Salmon is a rich source of brain-healthy omega-3 fatty acids, improving memory, supporting brain function, and preventing disease. Salmon also provides vitamins D, A, B, and minerals such as zinc, calcium, iron, and phosphorus. Salmon is helpful in maintaining cardiovascular health and lowering cholesterol, as well as aiding with glucose metabolism.

Mustard

Mustard is high in antioxidants and contains selenium, a mineral recognized for its anti-inflammatory properties. White mustard seed, which is the key ingredient in the familiar yellow condiment, is packed with omega-3 fatty acids, potassium, phosphorous, magnesium, and calcium. When consumed, these body beneficial substances work together to encourage the body to speed up metabolism, lower blood pressure and help prevent atherosclerosis.

Pork

Pork tenderloin rivals lean poultry as a healthy choice for complete protein. Pork tenderloin is as lean as a skinless chicken breast, and any cuts from the loin are even leaner than a skinless chicken thigh. Pork steaks or roasts from the leg (fresh ham) are also great choices. Pork is also an excellent source of B vitamins such as niacin, riboflavin, thiamin, and B-6.

Pecan-Crusted Chicken

INGREDIENTS

- 4 boneless skinless chicken breasts, 6 to 8 oz. each
- 1-1/2 teaspoons salt, divided
- 1 teaspoon lemon juice
- 1-1/2 cups plain yogurt
- 2 tablespoons Dijon mustard
- 2 cups pecans, finely chopped
- 1 cup bread crumbs
- Olive oil for sautéing

PREPARATION

- Use a mallet to pound chicken breasts into a uniform 1/2 inch thickness.
- Cut each breast into 2 or 3 pieces for manageability.
- Combine lemon juice, yogurt, mustard, and 1/2 teaspoon salt in a bowl and set aside.
- Put chicken pieces in mixture and let sit for about 10 minutes.
- Combine pecans, crumbs, and 1 teaspoon salt in a bowl and set aside.
- Heat about 1 tablespoon olive oil in a sauté pan over medium high heat. Wipe excess yogurt off chicken and dredge in pecan mixture. When oil is hot, add chicken pieces to pan and cook about 3–4 minutes on each side until golden brown on the outside and cooked through. You may need to do it in batches, in which case you should wipe the pan out between batches and add a bit more oil. Serve immediately.

Serves 4

Grilled Salmon with Mustard and Herbs

INGREDIENTS
- 2 lemons, thinly sliced, plus 1 lemon cut into wedges for garnish
- 20-30 sprigs mixed fresh herbs, plus 2 tablespoons chopped, divided
- 1 clove garlic
- 1/4 teaspoon salt
- 1 tablespoon Dijon mustard
- 1 pound center-cut salmon, skinned

PREPARATION
- Preheat grill to medium-high.
- Lay 2 9-inch pieces of heavy-duty foil on top of each other and place on a rimless baking sheet. Arrange lemon slices in two layers in the center of the foil. Spread herb sprigs over the lemons. With the side of a chef's knife, mash garlic with salt to form a paste. Transfer to a small dish and stir in mustard and the remaining 2 tablespoons of chopped herbs. Spread the mixture over both sides of the salmon. Place the salmon on the herb sprigs.
- Slide the foil and salmon off the baking sheet onto the grill without disturbing the salmon-lemon stack. Cover the grill; cook until the salmon is opaque in the center, 18 to 24 minutes. Wearing oven mitts, carefully transfer foil and salmon back onto the baking sheet. Cut the salmon into 4 portions and serve with lemon wedges (discard herb sprigs and lemon slices).

Serves 4

Seared Asian Tuna Steaks

INGREDIENTS

- 4 ahi tuna steaks (6-8 oz. each)
- Sesame oil
- 1/4 cup soy sauce
- 1 teaspoon Dijon mustard
- 1 shallot, finely grated
- 2 tablespoons honey
- 2 teaspoons fresh cracked pepper
- Sesame seeds for garnish

PREPARATION

- Combine 1 tablespoon sesame oil, soy sauce, mustard, shallot, honey, and pepper in a bowl and whisk together. Coat all sides of tuna steaks in marinade and let sit on counter for 30 minutes to 2 hours.
- Heat 2 teaspoons sesame oil in a non-stick grill pan or sauté pan over high heat.
- Sear tuna steaks on both sides, about 2 minutes per side. Sear edges about 30 seconds each (use tongs to hold the tuna on the sides to sear).
- Remove to plate. Sprinkle with sesame seeds and serve immediately.

Serves 4

Black Bean Quesadillas

INGREDIENTS

- 1 15-ounce can black beans, rinsed
- 1/2 cup shredded Monterey Jack cheese, preferably pepper Jack
- 1/2 cup prepared fresh salsa, divided
- 4 8-inch whole-wheat tortillas
- 2 teaspoons canola oil, divided
- 1 ripe avocado, diced

PREPARATION

- Combine beans, cheese, and 1/4 cup salsa in a medium bowl. Place tortillas on a work surface. Spread 1/2 cup filling on half of each tortilla. Fold tortillas in half, pressing gently to flatten.
- Heat 1 teaspoon oil in a large nonstick skillet over medium heat. Add 2 quesadillas and cook, turning once, until golden on both sides, 2 to 4 minutes total. Transfer to a cutting board and tent with foil to keep warm. Repeat with the remaining 1 teaspoon oil and quesadillas. Serve the quesadillas with avocado and the remaining salsa.

Serves 4

Mustard & Sage Grilled Pork Tenderloin

INGREDIENTS

- 1 pork tenderloin
- Splash white wine vinegar
- 2 heaping tablespoons Dijon mustard
- 2 heaping teaspoons ground sage
- 1 clove garlic, minced
- 3 tablespoons canola oil
- 10 fresh sage leaves
- Salt and pepper

PREPARATION

- Whisk together the mustard, sage, garlic, vinegar, and canola oil in a bowl. Add salt and pepper to taste.
- Place pork tenderloin in a dish, coat with mustard mixture, and marinate for 30 minutes to 1 hour.
- Heat barbeque grill over high heat. Grease grill and place tenderloin directly on grill.
- On the side facing up, place 5 sage leaves face down and press into meat. Cook on high for approximately 4 minutes, then flip tenderloin over.
- Turn heat down to medium and line second side of the tenderloin with remaining sage leaves face down.
- Continue cooking, turning occasionally until the interior of the tenderloin reads 155°F
- Remove from heat, cover, and let rest for 10 minutes. Slice and serve.

Serves 2-4

DESSERTS

When creating a brain-healthy diet, dessert deprivation isn't required. You can still enjoy desserts for an ageless mind - just pay attention to what the dessert adds to the foods you've consumed that day. Some desserts offer health benefits, while others simply add calories. Choose desserts that fulfill your dietary needs to ensure you don't feel deprived while working toward healthy nutrition.

By choosing healthy desserts, you fulfill your need for indulgence and also add nutrients to your overall eating plan. "Indulgence is not necessarily a bad thing," says Dr. Jeffrey Heit, a clinical instructor with the University of Pennsylvania School of Medicine. "Just make sure it all fits into the larger health picture."

Featured Ingredients

Vanilla

Vanilla extract has a number of health benefits such as being associated with reducing stress and anxiety and helping aid weight loss. Vanilla is a natural calming agent, and it is great to digest small amounts before bed. Keep in mind that a little goes a long way with vanilla extract. Limit to a few drops in individual servings of warm drinks or baked goods.

Dark Chocolate

Since chocolate comes from a plant, it offers some of the same health benefits as dark vegetables. Like other plants, it contains flavonoids, which provide beneficial antioxidants to the body. Eating dark chocolate in moderation can lessen the damage of free radicals that contribute to heart disease and cause the body to age faster. When buying chocolate, look for the highest percentage of cocoa available.

Blueberries

Often touted as the perfect brain food, these tiny little gems do indeed pack a potent punch. They rank high on the list of antioxidants, and one cup delivers 14% of the recommended daily dose of fiber and nearly 25% of the recommended daily intake of vitamin C. Blueberries are also good for the wasitline, with fewer than 100 calories per cup.

Vanilla Lemon-Berry Parfait

INGREDIENTS

- 1 cup plain low-fat yogurt
- 2 (3.5 ounce) containers fat-free vanilla pudding
- 2 tablespoons bottled lemon curd (such as Dickinson's)
- 1/2 teaspoon vanilla extract
- 2 tablespoons honey
- Zest of 1 lemon
- 1 tablespoon fresh lemon juice
- 3 cups mixed berries (such as blueberries, strawberries, and raspberries)
- Fresh mint leaves (optional)

PREPARATION

- In a small mixing bowl, whisk together the yogurt, pudding, lemon curd, and vanilla extract; set aside.
- In a medium mixing bowl, stir the honey, lemon zest, and lemon juice until combined. Add the mixed berries, and gently stir with a rubber spatula to coat them with the honey mixture.
- Assemble the parfaits in 4 (8-ounce) glasses. Using measuring spoons, scoop 3 tablespoons of the yogurt mixture into each glass. Top with 1/4 cup of the berries, then another 3 tablespoons yogurt, and another 1/4 cup berries. Garnish each yogurt parfait with fresh mint, if desired. Serve immediately, or cover and refrigerate for up to 2 hours.

Serves 4

Banana Oatmeal Chocolate Chip Cookies

INGREDIENTS

- 1/2 cup whole wheat flour
- 1 cup rolled oats (not instant)
- 1/2 tsp baking powder
- 1/2 tsp baking soda
- 1/4 tsp cinnamon
- 1 Tbsp ground flaxseed meal
- 1/4 cup agave nectar
- 1/4 cup soy milk (can substitute regular milk)
- 1/2 tsp vanilla extract
- 1 Tbsp canola oil
- 1 ripe banana
- 1/2 cup dark chocolate chips
- 1/4 cup walnuts, chopped

PREPARATION

- Preheat oven to 350°F.
- Combine all ingredients in a large bowl. Mix well until batter is blended evenly.
- Use a tablespoon to portion cookies on a greased baking sheet, approximately 1-2 inches apart.
- Bake cookies for 12-15 minutes.
- Remove cookies from baking sheet and allow to cool on wire rack.

Makes 2 dozen

Blueberry and Peach Crisp

INGREDIENTS

- 3 large peaches
- Canola oil spray
- 3 cups blueberries
- 3-1/2 tablespoons whole wheat flower
- 3/4 cup wheat germ
- 1/4 cup turbinado sugar
- 1-1/2 tablespoons canola oil
- 1/4 teaspoon vanilla extract

PREPARATION

- Preheat oven to 350°F
- Chop the peaches into 1/2 inch bite-sized cubes. Place in a canola-sprayed, 8x8 inch baking dish along with blueberries.
- Sprinkle 2 tablespoons of the whole wheat flour over the fruits and mix to coat.
- In a small mixing bowl, combine the remaining ingredients and cover the fruits.
- Bake for 20 minutes or until the topping is golden brown and the liquid of the fruit bubbles. Remove from the oven and let stand for 10 minutes before serving.

Serves 8

Dark Chocolate Mousse

INGREDIENTS

- 5-1/4 ounces bittersweet chocolate, coarsely chopped
- 14 ounces cold heavy cream
- 3 large egg whites
- 1 ounce sugar
- Sweetened whipped cream, for garnish (optional)
- Shaved bittersweet chocolate, for garnish (optional)

PREPARATION

- Place chocolate in a large bowl set over a bain marie or in a double boiler at a low simmer. Stir chocolate until melted. Turn off the heat and let stand.
- Beat the cream over ice until it forms soft peaks. Set aside and hold at room temperature. With a mixer, whip egg whites. Gradually add the sugar and continue whipping until firm.
- Remove the chocolate from the bain marie and using a whisk, fold in the egg whites all at once. When the whites are almost completely incorporated, fold in the whipped cream. Cover the mousse and refrigerate for approximately 1 hour or until set. Serve in goblets topped with more whipped cream and shaved chocolate, if desired.

Serves 4-6

Blueberry Walnut Scones

INGREDIENTS

- 1/2 cup oats
- 1 cup all-purpose flour
- 1 cup whole wheat flour
- 1/3 cup packed brown sugar
- 2 teaspoons lemon zest, minced
- 1-1/2 teaspoons baking powder
- 1/2 teaspoon baking soda
- 1/4 teaspoon salt
- 6 tablespoons chilled butter, cut into small cubes
- 1 cup roughly chopped walnuts
- 3/4 cup dried blueberries
- 2/3 cup buttermilk
- 1 egg

PREPARATION

- Preheat oven to 400°F. In a large bowl, combine oats, flours, sugar, zest, baking powder, baking soda, and salt. Add butter and use your fingers or a pastry cutter to rub butter into dry ingredients until mixture resembles coarse meal. Stir in walnuts and blueberries.

- Lightly beat buttermilk and egg together. Stir into flour mixture just until evenly combined. Divide dough in half and form each half into a disk. Use a pastry cutter or sharp knife to cut each disk into 6 triangles. Place on a baking sheet and bake for 15 minutes or until scones are cooked through. Cool on a wire rack.

Makes 12

A Healthy Diet and Your Ageless Mind

You are what you eat, and that includes your brain. Food powers the body and fuels the mind, so whatever you eat or drink will have a direct affect upon your physical and mental well-being. If you make smart dietary choices, you will give your brain the fuel it needs to run healthy and strong. If you don't eat properly, your brain will begin to function less efficiently, potentially resulting in poor concentration, cognitive impairment, and memory loss.

While this book provides a starting point, I encourage you to talk with your doctor or a nutrition specialist to discuss a long-term strategy. When it comes to your health, both knowledge and preparation are needed to provide a bright future for you and your ageless mind.

RECOMMENDED **READING**

Recommended Reading

We are grateful to the many doctors, scientists, and researchers who are cited in the references section of this book, and we recommend that you explore their work in more depth. These resources will directly help you improve your ageless mind. In the interest of space, the list has been limited to just one book per author, however, many of the authors have numerous books and articles whose valuable information has been featured in this book. When available, the author's website has been provided and is current as of this printing.

Andreasen, Nancy C. The Creating Brain: The Neuroscience of Genius. New York: Dana, 2005.

Agronin, Marc E. *How We Age: A doctor's journey into the Heart of Growing Old.* Cambridge, MA: Da Capo Press, 2011. Website:www.marcargonin.com.

Amen, Daniel G. *Magnificent Mind at Any Age: Natural Ways to Unleash Your Brain's Maximum Potential.* New York: Three Rivers Press, 2009. Website: www.amenclinics. com.

Benson, Herbert. *The Relaxation Response.* New York: Morrow, 1975. Website: www. relaxationresponse.com.

Bortz, Walter M., and Randall Stickrod. *The Roadmap to 100: The Breakthrough Science of Living a Long and Healthy Life.* New York: Palgrave Macmillan, 2010. Website: www.walterbortz.com.

Brown, Stuart L., and Christopher C. Vaughan. *Play: How It Shapes the Brain, Opens Imagination, and Invigorates the Soul.* New York: Avery, 2010

Buzan, Tony. *The Mind Map Book.* New York: Dutton, 1994. Website: www.thinkbuzan. com.

Cass, Hyla, and Patrick Holford. *Natural Highs: Supplements, Nutrition, and Mind-Body Techniques to Help You Feel Good All the Time.* New York: Avery, 2002. Website: www.cassmd.com.

Childre, Doc, and Howard Martin. *The HeartMath Solution: The Institute of Hartmath's Revolutionary Program for Engaging the Power of the Heart's Intelligence.* San Francisco: HarperSanFrancisco, 2000. Website: www.heartmath.com.

Chopra, Deepak, and David Simon. *Grow Younger: 10 Steps to Reverse Aging.* New York: Harmony Books, 2001. Website: www.chopra.com.

Cohen, Gene. *The Mature Mind: The Positive Power of the Aging Brain.* New York: Basic Books, 2006.

Crook III, Thomas H. *The Memory Cure: The Safe, Scientifically Proven Breakthrough That Can Slow, Halt, or Even Reverse Age-Related Memory Loss.* New York: Pocket Books,1998.

Damasio, Antonio. *Descartes' Error: Emotion, Reason, and the Human Brain.* New York: Putnam, 1994.

Dement, William C. and Christopher C. Vaughan. *The Promise of Sleep: a Pioneer in Sleep Medicine Explores the Vital Connection Between Health, Happiness, and a Good Night's Sleep.* New York: Dell Trade Paperback, 2000.

Doidge, Norman. *The Brain that Changes Itself: Stories of Triumph from the Frontiers of Brain Science.* New York: Penguin, 2007. Website: www.normandoidge.com.

Dychtwald, Ken. *The Agewave: How the Most Important Trend of Our Time Can Change Your Future.* New York, Bantam, 1990. Website: www.dychtwald.com.

Edlund, Mathew. *The Power of Rest: Why Sleep Alone is Not Enough. A 30-Day Plan to Reset Your Body.* New York: HarperOne, 2010. Website: www.therestdoctor.com.

Fehmi, Les, and Jim Robbins. *The Open-Focus Brain: Harnessing the Power of Attention to Heal Mind and Body.* Boston: Trumpeter Books, 2007. Website: www.openfocus. com.

Gardner, Howard. *Frames of Mind: The Theory of Multiple Intelligence.* New York: Basic, 2011.

Hutchison, Michael. *Megabrain: New Tools and Techniques for Brain Growth and Mind Expansion.* New York: Ballantine Books, 1996.

Kabat-Zinn, Jon. *Wherever You Go, There You Are: Mindfulness Meditations in Everyday Life*. New York: Hyperion, 1994. Website: www.mindfulnesstapes.com.

Khalsa, Dharma Singh. *Brain Longevity: The Breakthrough Medical Program That Improves Your Mind and Memory*. New York: Grand Central Publishing, 1999.

Kornblatt, Sondra. *A Better Brain at Any Age.: The Holistic Way to Improve Your Memory, Reduce Stress, and Sharpen Your Wits*. San Francisco, CA: Red Wheel /Weiser, 2008.

Langer, Ellen J. *Counterclockwise: Mindful Health and the Power of Possibility*. New York: Ballantine Books, 2009. Website: www.ellenlanger.com.

Lipton, Bruce H. *The Biology of Belief; Unleashing the Power of Consciousness, Matter, and Miracles*. Santa Rosa, CA: Elite Books, 2005. Website: www.brucelipton.com

McEwen, Bruce S., and Elizabeth Norton Lasley. *The End Of Stress as We Know It*. Washington, D.C.: Joseph Henry Press, 2002.

Medina, John. *Brain Rules: 12 Principles for Surviving and Thriving at Work, Home, and School*. Seattle: Pear Press, 2008. Website: www.brainrules.com.

Pink, Daniel H. *A Whole New Mind: Why Right-Brainers Will Rule the Future*. New York: Riverhead Books, 2006. Website: www.danpink.com.

Ranck, Chris. *Ignite the Genius Within: Discover Your Full Potential*. New York: Plume, 2010. Website: www.christineranck.com.

Ratey, John J. *Spark: The Revolutionary New Science of Exercise and the Brain*. New York: Little, Brown, 2008. Website: www.johnratey.com

Restak, Richard. *Mozart's Brain and the Fighter Pilot: Unleashing Your Brain's Potential*. New York: Three Rivers Press, 2002. Website: www.richardrestak.com.

Roizen, Michael F., and Mehmet C. Oz. *YOU: Staying Young; The Owner's Manual for Extending Your Warranty*. New York: Free Press, 2007. Website: www.realage.com.

Russell, Peter. *The Brain Book: Know Your Mind and How to Use It*. London: Routledge, 1994. Website: www.peterrussell.com.

Schwartz, Jeffrey M., and Sharon Begley. *The Mind and the Brain: Neuroplasticity and the Power of Mental Force*. New York: ReganBooks, 2002.

Sears, Al. *PACE: The 12-Minute Fitness Revolution*. Royal Palm Beach, FL: Wellness Research Foundation, 2010. Website: www.alsearsmd.com.

Selhub, Eva. *The Love Response: Your Prescription to Turn Off Fear, Anger, and Anxiety to Achieve Vibrant Health and Transform Your Life*. New York: Ballantine Books, 2009. Website: www.drselhub.com.

Seligman, Martin E. P. *Learned Optimism: How to Change Your Mind and Your Life*. New York: Pocket Books, 1998. Website: www.ppc.sas.upenn.edu.

Siegel, Bernie S. *Love, Medicine and Miracles: Lessons Learned about Self-Healing from a Surgeon's Experience with Exceptional Patients*. New York: HarperPerennial, 1990. Website: www.berniesiegelmd.com.

Victoroff, Jeff. *Saving Your Brain: The Revolutionary Plan to Boost Brain Power, Improve Memory, and Protecting Yourself Against Aging and Alzheimer's Disease*. New York: Bantam, 2002.

Weil, Andrew. *Healthy Aging: A Lifelong Guide to Your Physical and Spiritual Well-Being*. New York: Knopf, 2005. Website: www.drweil.com.

Whalley, Lawrence. *The Aging Brain*. New York: Columbia University Press, 2001.

Made in the USA
Charleston, SC
10 July 2013